Polished Spiral Karin Kuhlmann

"Although the creation of fractals is bounded to strict mathematical rules, the results are always very inspiring."– **Karin Kuhlmann**

GRADE

4

Factors, Multiples, and Arrays

Multiplication and Division 1   UNIT 1

Investigations

IN NUMBER, DATA, AND SPACE®

PEARSON
Scott
Foresman
scottforesman.com

Editorial offices: Glenview, Illinois • Parsippany, New Jersey • New York, New York
Sales offices: Boston, Massachusetts • Duluth, Georgia
Glenview, Illinois • Coppell, Texas • Sacramento, California • Mesa, Arizona

T E R C

The Investigations curriculum was developed by TERC, Cambridge, MA.

NSF

This material is based on work supported by the National Science Foundation ("NSF") under Grant No. ESI-0095450. Any opinions, findings, and conclusions or recommendations expressed in this material are those of the author(s) and do not necessarily reflect the views of the National Science Foundation.

ISBN: 0-328-23753-1

ISBN: 978-0-328-23753-1

Second Edition Copyright © 2008 Pearson Education, Inc.
All Rights Reserved. Printed in the United States of America. This publication is protected by Copyright, and permission should be obtained from the publisher prior to any prohibited reproduction, storage in a retrieval system, or transmission in any form by any means, electronic, mechanical, photocopying, recording, or otherwise. For information regarding permission(s), write to: Permissions Department, Scott Foresman, 1900 East Lake Avenue, Glenview, Illinois 60025.

8 9 10-V003-15 14 13 12 11 10 09 08

CC:N2

T E R C

Co-Principal Investigators

Susan Jo Russell

Karen Economopoulos

Authors

Lucy Wittenberg
Director Grades 3–5

Karen Economopoulos
Director Grades K–2

Virginia Bastable
(SummerMath for Teachers,
Mt. Holyoke College)

Katie Hickey Bloomfield

Keith Cochran

Darrell Earnest

Arusha Hollister

Nancy Horowitz

Erin Leidl

Megan Murray

Young Oh

Beth W. Perry

Susan Jo Russell

Deborah Schifter
(Education
Development Center)

Kathy Sillman

Administrative Staff

Amy Taber
Project Manager

Beth Bergeron

Lorraine Brooks

Emi Fujiwara

Contributing Authors

Denise Baumann

Jennifer DiBrienza

Hollee Freeman

Paula Hooper

Jan Mokros

Stephen Monk
(University of Washington)

Mary Beth O'Connor

Judy Storeygard

Cornelia Tierney

Elizabeth Van Cleef

Carol Wright

Technology

Jim Hammerman

Classroom Field Work

Amy Appell

Rachel E. Davis

Traci Higgins

Julia Thompson

Collaborating Teachers

This group of dedicated teachers carried out extensive field testing in their classrooms, met regularly to discuss issues of teaching and learning mathematics, provided feedback to staff, welcomed staff into their classrooms to document students' work, and contributed both suggestions and written material that has been incorporated into the curriculum.

Bethany Altchek	Maura McGrail
Linda Amaral	Kathe Millett
Kimberly Beauregard	Florence Molyneaux
Barbara Bernard	Amy Monkiewicz
Nancy Buell	Elizabeth Monopoli
Rose Christiansen	Carol Murray
Chris Colbath-Hess	Robyn Musser
Lisette Colon	Christine Norrman
Kim Cook	Deborah O'Brien
Frances Cooper	Timothy O'Connor
Kathleen Drew	Anne Marie O'Reilly
Rebeka Eston Salemi	Mark Paige
Thomas Fisher	Margaret Riddle
Michael Flynn	Karen Schweitzer
Holly Ghazey	Elisabeth Seyferth
Susan Gillis	Susan Smith
Danielle Harrington	Debra Sorvillo
Elaine Herzog	Shoshanah Starr
Francine Hiller	Janice Szymaszek
Kirsten Lee Howard	Karen Tobin
Liliana Klass	JoAnn Trauschke
Leslie Kramer	Ana Vaisenstein
Melissa Lee Andrichak	Yvonne Watson
Kelley Lee Sadowski	Michelle Woods
Jennifer Levitan	Mary Wright
Mary Lou LoVecchio	
Kristen McEnaney	

Note: Unless otherwise noted, all contributors listed above were staff of the Education Research Collaborative at TERC during their work on the curriculum. Other affiliations during the time of development are listed.

Advisors

Deborah Lowenberg Ball,
University of Michigan

Hyman Bass, Professor of Mathematics and Mathematics Education
University of Michigan

Mary Canner, Principal, Natick Public Schools

Thomas Carpenter, Professor of Curriculum and Instruction,
University of Wisconsin-Madison

Janis Freckmann, Elementary Mathematics Coordinator,
Milwaukee Public Schools

Lynne Godfrey, Mathematics Coach,
Cambridge Public Schools

Ginger Hanlon, Instructional Specialist in Mathematics,
New York City Public Schools

DeAnn Huinker, Director, Center for Mathematics and
Science Education Research, University of Wisconsin-Milwaukee

James Kaput, Professor of Mathematics, University of
Massachusetts-Dartmouth

Kate Kline, Associate Professor, Department of Mathematics
and Statistics, Western Michigan University

Jim Lewis, Professor of Mathematics,
University of Nebraska-Lincoln

William McCallum, Professor of Mathematics,
University of Arizona

Harriet Pollatsek, Professor of Mathematics,
Mount Holyoke College

Debra Shein-Gerson, Elementary Mathematics Specialist,
Weston Public Schools

Gary Shevell, Assistant Principal,
New York City Public Schools

Liz Sweeney, Elementary Math Department,
Boston Public Schools

Lucy West, Consultant, Metamorphosis:
Teaching Learning Communities, Inc.

This revision of the curriculum was built on the work of the many authors who contributed to the first edition (published between 1994 and 1998). We acknowledge the critical contributions of these authors in developing the content and pedagogy of *Investigations*:

Authors

Joan Akers

Michael T. Battista

Douglas H. Clements

Karen Economopoulos

Marlene Kliman

Jan Mokros

Megan Murray

Ricardo Nemirovsky

Andee Rubin

Susan Jo Russell

Cornelia Tierney

Contributing Authors

Mary Berle-Carman

Rebecca B. Corwin

Rebeka Eston

Claryce Evans

Anne Goodrow

Cliff Konold

Chris Mainhart

Sue McMillen

Jerrie Moffet

Tracy Noble

Kim O'Neil

Mark Ogonowski

Julie Sarama

Amy Shulman Weinberg

Margie Singer

Virginia Woolley

Tracey Wright

Contents

UNIT 1

Factors, Multiples, and Arrays

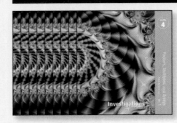

Investigations

CURRICULUM

Overview of Program Components

FOR TEACHERS

The **Curriculum Units** are the teaching guides. (See far right.)

Implementing Investigations in Grade 4 offers suggestions for implementing the curriculum. It also contains a comprehensive index.

The **Resources Binder** contains all the Resource Masters and Transparencies that support instruction. (Also available on CD) The binder also includes a student software CD.

FOR STUDENTS

The **Student Activity Book** contains the consumable student pages (Recording Sheets, Homework, Practice, and so on).

The **Student Math Handbook** contains Math Words and Ideas pages and Games directions.

The *Investigations* Curriculum

Investigations in Number, Data, and Space® is a K–5 mathematics curriculum designed to engage students in making sense of mathematical ideas. Six major goals guided the development of the *Investigations in Number, Data, and Space®* curriculum. The curriculum is designed to:

- Support students to make sense of mathematics and learn that they can be mathematical thinkers

- Focus on computational fluency with whole numbers as a major goal of the elementary grades

- Provide substantive work in important areas of mathematics—rational numbers, geometry, measurement, data, and early algebra—and connections among them

- Emphasize reasoning about mathematical ideas

- Communicate mathematics content and pedagogy to teachers

- Engage the range of learners in understanding mathematics

Underlying these goals are three guiding principles that are touchstones for the *Investigations* team as we approach both students and teachers as agents of their own learning:

1. *Students have mathematical ideas.* Students come to school with ideas about numbers, shapes, measurements, patterns, and data. If given the opportunity to learn in an environment that stresses making sense of mathematics, students build on the ideas they already have and learn about new mathematics they have never encountered. Students learn that they are capable of having mathematical ideas, applying what they know to new situations, and thinking and reasoning about unfamiliar problems.

2. *Teachers are engaged in ongoing learning* about mathematics content, pedagogy, and student learning. The curriculum provides material for professional development, to be used by teachers individually or in groups, that supports teachers' continued learning as they use the curriculum over several years. The *Investigations* curriculum materials are designed as much to be a dialogue with teachers as to be a core of content for students.

3. *Teachers collaborate with the students and curriculum materials* to create the curriculum as enacted in the classroom. The only way for a good curriculum to be used well is for teachers to be active participants in implementing it. Teachers use the curriculum to maintain a clear, focused, and coherent agenda for mathematics teaching. At the same time, they observe and listen carefully to students, try to understand how they are thinking, and make teaching decisions based on these observations.

Investigations is based on experience from research and practice, including field testing that involved documentation of thousands of hours in classrooms, observations of students, input from teachers, and analysis of student work. As a result, the curriculum addresses the learning needs of real students in a wide range of classrooms and communities. The investigations are carefully designed to invite all students into mathematics—girls and boys; members of diverse cultural, ethnic, and language groups; and students with a wide variety of strengths, needs, and interests.

Based on this extensive classroom testing, the curriculum takes seriously the time students need to develop a strong conceptual foundation and skills based on that foundation. Each curriculum unit focuses on an area of content in depth, providing time for students to develop and practice ideas across a variety of activities and contexts that build on each other. Daily guidelines for time spent on class sessions, Classroom Routines (K–3), and Ten-Minute Math (3–5) reflect the commitment to devoting adequate time to mathematics in each school day.

About This Curriculum Unit

This **Curriculum Unit** is one of nine teaching guides in Grade 4. The first unit in Grade 4 is *Factors, Multiples, and Arrays*.

- The **Introduction and Overview** section organizes and presents the instructional materials, provides background information, and highlights important features specific to this unit.

- Each Curriculum Unit contains several **Investigations.** Each Investigation focuses on a set of related mathematical ideas.

- Investigations are divided into one-hour **Sessions,** or lessons.

- Sessions have a combination of these parts: **Activity, Discussion, Math Workshop, Assessment Activity,** and **Session Follow-Up.**

- Each session also has one or more **Ten-Minute Math activities** that are done outside of math time.

- At the back of the book is a collection of **Teacher Notes** and **Dialogue Boxes** that provide professional development related to the unit.

- Also included at the back of the book are the **Student Math Handbook** pages for this unit.

- The **Index** provides a way to look up important words or terms.

Overview

O F   T H I S   U N I T

Investigation	Session	Day	
INVESTIGATION 1 **Representing Multiplication with Arrays** Students use arrays to represent multiplication situations. They use arrays to find factors and gain fluency with multiplication combinations up to 12 × 12.	**1.1** Things That Come in Arrays	1	
	1.2 Making Arrays	2	
	1.3 Making Arrays, *continued*	3	
	1.4 Which Combinations Do I Know?	4	
	1.5 Using Arrays to Multiply	5	
INVESTIGATION 2 **Multiplication Combinations** Students develop strategies for finding factors and multiples of 2- and 3-digit numbers. They continue to gain fluency with multiplication combinations up to 12 × 12.	**2.1** Quick Images	6	
	2.2 Multiplication Cards	7	
	2.3 Multiple Turn Over	8	
	2.4 Multiplication Combinations	9	
	2.5 Assessment: Multiplication Combinations	10	
INVESTIGATION 3 **Finding Factors** Students use what they know about the factors of 100 to find factors of multiples of 100. They explore the idea that factors of a number are also factors of a multiple of that number.	**3.1** Factors of 100	11	
	3.2 Factors of the Multiples of 100	12	
	3.3 Factors of Related Numbers	13	
	3.4 End-of-Unit Assessment	14	

Each *Investigations* session has some combination of these five parts: **Activity, Discussion, Math Workshop, Assessment Activity,** and **Session Follow-Up.** These session parts are indicated in the chart below. Each session also has one or more **Ten-Minute Math** activities that are done outside of math time.

Ten-Minute Math

Activity	Discussion	Math Workshop	Assessment Activity	Session Follow-Up		Today's Number	Quick Images	Counting Around the Class
●	●			●		●		
● ●				●		●		
● ●	●			●		●		
● ●	●			●		●		
	●	●	●	●		●		
● ●	●			●			●	
●				●			●	
● ● ●				●			●	
	●	●		●			●	
		●	●	●			●	
● ● ●	●			●			●	
●	● ●			●				●
●	●			●				●
			●	●				●

Mathematics

Factors, Multiples, and Arrays, which focuses on the operation of multiplication, is the first Grade 4 unit in the number and operations strand of *Investigations.* These units develop ideas about the meaning of operations with whole numbers, the development of computational fluency, the structure of place value and the base-ten number system, and generalizations about numbers and operations.

LOOKING BACK

In early grades, students began thinking about ideas of multiplication as they counted by numbers other than 1 and solved problems involving equal groups. They worked with division situations as they solved problems about sharing a variety of objects equally and making equal-sized groups. In Grade 3, students' work focused on understanding that multiplication is used to combine a number of equal-sized groups and that division is used when the product is known and either the number of equal-sized groups or the size of those groups must be determined. Students were introduced to arrays as rectangular arrangements of objects in rows and columns (24 chairs can be arranged in 4 rows of 6, or 2 rows of 12). They worked on developing fluency with multiplication combinations by skip counting on 100 charts and through games and activities with a set of Array Cards representing products up to 50.

The work in this unit assumes that students understand that multiplication involves equal groups. They should recognize arrays as a model for multiplication and be able to relate skip counting to creating equal groups. It is also expected that most students know the multiplication combinations with products to 50 and can find the factors of numbers to 50. This unit builds directly on all of these ideas.

This unit focuses on 3 Mathematical Emphases:

1 Whole Number Operations Understanding and working with an array model of multiplication

Math Focus Points

◆ Using arrays to model multiplication situations

◆ Breaking an array into parts to find the product represented by the array

◆ Using arrays to find factors of 2-digit numbers

◆ Identifying features of numbers, including prime, square, and composite numbers

As students develop strategies to use in solving multiplication and division problems, it is critical that they develop visual images that support their work. Students use rectangular arrays to represent the relationship between a product and its factors: the area of the array is the product, and the length and width of the rectangle are one pair of factors of that product.

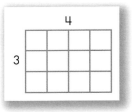

Array representing
3 × 4 = 12

Through using an array model, students visualize important multiplication relationships. For example, the solution to 7 × 6 is the same as the solution to 6 × 7, and the product represented by a larger array can be found by breaking it apart into smaller arrays.

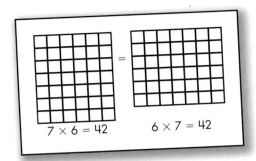

Students consider features of numbers (including prime, square, and composite numbers) by examining all the arrays for a particular product. In addition, students relate their understanding of multiplication as involving equal groups to their work with arrays. For example, in a 6×8 array, they see that each row contains 8 units and that there are 6 rows or groups.

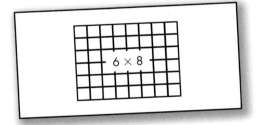

2 Whole Number Operations Reasoning about numbers and their factors

Math Focus Points

◆ Finding the multiples of a number by skip counting

◆ Determining whether one number is a factor or multiple of another

◆ Identifying the factors of a given number

◆ Identifying all the factors of 100

◆ Using knowledge of the factors of 100 to find factors of multiples of 100

◆ Using known multiplication combinations to find related multiplication combinations for a given product (e.g., if $4 \times 50 = 200$, then $8 \times 25 = 200$)

◆ Using representations to show that a factor of a number is also a factor of its multiples (e.g., if 25 is a factor of 100, then 25 is also a factor of 300)

A great deal of work in this unit focuses on working with factors and multiples so that students become familiar with number relationships that they can use as part of their repertoire for solving problems. In this unit, students identify the factors of given numbers, compare the factors of a number with factors of multiples of that number (e.g., factors of 16 and factors of 48), and generate the multiples of numbers through skip counting.

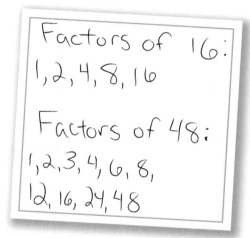

Sample Student Work

Students generate the factors of 100 and then use those factors to solve problems involving larger numbers. As students use the knowledge that $5 \times 20 = 100$ to determine how many 20s are in 200, 300, and so on, they are developing important tools for solving multidigit multiplication and division problems. In later work, when students encounter a problem such as $425 \div 22 = \underline{\quad}$, they can use their knowledge that 100 is composed of five 20s to quickly determine that a reasonable answer to this problem will be close to 20 because there are five 20s in each of the four 100s. Sometimes, such estimates are all that is needed in practical situations. At other times, these estimates serve as an important check that the solution to the problem is reasonable and does not contain place-value errors.

Reasoning about numbers and their factors also helps students learn more about the properties of the operation of multiplication. For example, they notice that they can sometimes generate additional factors of a number by doubling and halving a pair of factors they already know (because $2 \times 150 = 300$, 4×75 also equals 300). This is an idea that they will pursue in more depth in the second multiplication and division unit in Grade 4.

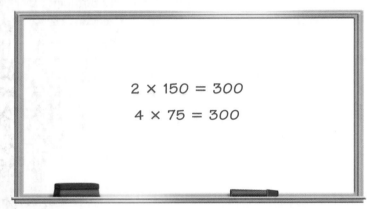

$$2 \times 150 = 300$$

$$4 \times 75 = 300$$

Students also notice that if, for example, 6 is a factor of a number, then 3 is also a factor of that number. In Investigation 3, they explore this particular idea: that the factors of a number are also factors of any multiple of that number.

Through this work with factors and multiples, students are learning more about how multiplication behaves and how numbers in a multiplication problem can be manipulated to solve the problem. The more fluent and flexible students become in their understanding of the relationships between numbers and their factors, the more knowledge they have to apply in many multiplication and division situations.

3 Computational Fluency Fluency with multiplication combinations to 12 × 12

Math Focus Points

◆ Identifying and learning multiplication combinations not yet known fluently

◆ Using known multiplication combinations to determine the products of more difficult combinations

A key element of developing computational fluency for whole number multiplication is knowledge of the basic multiplication combinations (known traditionally as "facts"). In this unit, students use combinations they know to solve more difficult problems. For example, they consider how knowing the product of 3×7 can help them solve 6×7 because the product of 3×7 is half the product of 6×7. They also might use their knowledge of multiplying by 10 to find the product of a number multiplied by 9, such as: $9 \times 9 = (10 \times 9) - 9$.

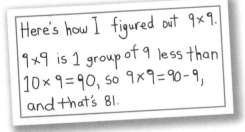

Here's how I figured out 9×9.
9×9 is 1 group of 9 less than
10 × 9 = 90, so 9×9=90-9,
and that's 81.

Sample Student Work

These strategies, which involve examining and understanding the relationships among factors, help students learn the more difficult multiplication combinations and support their later work with multidigit multiplication and division.

Ten-Minute Math activities focus on

◆ Generating equivalent expressions for a number using particular constraints

◆ Practicing computation skills

◆ Using notation to record expressions

◆ Organizing and analyzing visual images

◆ Writing equations to represent the total number of dots in a pattern

◆ Finding the multiples of numbers through skip counting

◆ Becoming familiar with multiplication patterns

◆ Understanding the relationship between skip counting and multiplication

LOOKING FORWARD In Grade 4, students continue to work on multiplication and division in *Multiple Towers and Division Stories* and *How Many Packages? How Many Groups?* In these units, students work on developing strategies for solving multiplication problems with larger numbers and extend the work with division they began in Grade 3. These units emphasize keeping track of all the parts of multiplication and division problems involving multidigit numbers. In Grade 5, students consolidate their strategies for both multiplication and division as they continue to study the properties of both operations.

Assessment

IN THIS UNIT

ONGOING ASSESSMENT: Observing Students at Work

The following sessions provide **Ongoing Assessment: Observing Students at Work** opportunities:

- **Session 1.1, p. 30**
- **Session 1.2, p. 36**
- **Session 1.4, p. 45**
- **Session 1.5, pp. 49 and 50**

- **Session 2.1, p. 62**
- **Session 2.2, p. 66**
- **Session 2.3, pp. 71 and 74**
- **Session 2.5, p. 83**

- **Session 3.1, pp. 91 and 94**
- **Session 3.2, p. 100**
- **Session 3.3, p. 107**

WRITING OPPORTUNITIES

The following sessions have **writing** opportunities for students to explain their mathematical thinking:

- **Session 1.5, pp. 48–49**
  Student Activity Book, pp. 11–12
- **Session 3.3, p. 107**
  Student Activity Book, p. 40
- **Sessions 3.3, p. 111**
  Student Activity Book, p. 41

PORTFOLIO OPPORTUNITIES

The following sessions have work appropriate for a **portfolio:**

- **Session 1.1, p. 28**
  Student Activity Book, p. 2
- **Session 1.5, p. 49**
  Student Activity Book, p. 12

- **Session 1.5, p. 50**
  M31, Assessment: Representing 8×6
- **Session 2.5, p. 81**
  M51, Assessment: Multiplication Combinations

- **Session 3.2, p. 98**
  Student Activity Book, pp. 33–34
- **Session 3.4, p. 113**
  M55–M56, End-of-Unit Assessment

Assessing the Benchmarks

Observing students as they engage in conversation about their ideas is a primary means to assess their mathematical understanding. Consider all of your students' work, not just the written assessments. See the chart below for suggestions about key activities to observe.

☑ Checklist Available

Benchmarks in This Unit	Key Activities to Observe	Assessment
1. Use known multiplication combinations to find the product of any multiplication combination up to 12 × 12.	**Sessions 1.4 and 1.5:** *Factor Pairs* **Session 2.2:** Multiplication Cards	**Session 2.5:** Assessment: Multiplication Combinations **Session 3.4:** End-of-Unit Assessment: Problem 1A
2. Use arrays, pictures or models of groups, and story contexts to represent multiplication situations.	**Sessions 1.2 and 1.3:** Making Arrays	**Session 1.5:** Assessment: Representing 8 × 6 ☑ **Session 3.4:** End-of-Unit Assessment: Problems 1B and 1C
3. Find the factors of 2-digit numbers.	**Sessions 1.2 and 1.3:** Making Arrays **Session 3.3:** Factors of 16 and 48	**Session 3.4:** End-of-Unit Assessment: Problem 2

Relating the Mathematical Emphases to the Benchmarks

Mathematical Emphases	Benchmarks
Whole Number Operations Understanding and working with an array model of multiplication	**2 and 3**
Whole Number Operations Reasoning about numbers and their factors	**3**
Computational Fluency Fluency with multiplication combinations to 12 × 12	**1**

In this unit, your students will have opportunities to engage with ideas that lay a foundation for algebra. Nine- and ten-year-olds can and do think algebraically. Part of the work of Grade 4 is helping students learn to verbalize and represent those thoughts both as a way to engage with generalizations about numbers and operations, and as a foundation for meaningful use of algebraic notation in the future. **Note:** Although algebraic notation is not introduced in this unit, students will work with notation in Unit 9, *Penny Jars and Plant Growth.*

Using the Distributive Property

Consider the following vignette:

A teacher asks students to explain how they figured out 12×9.

Enrique: First, I did $10 \times 9 = 90$, and then I did $2 \times 9 = 18$. $90 + 18 = 108$.

Helena: I did 6×9 and then 6×9 again, so I got $54 + 54 = 108$.

Teacher: You had different ways to show that $12 \times 9 = 108$. Can you explain how you know your method works? How can you use story contexts or diagrams to show why your method works?

When given a multiplication combination that they do not know, both students built up to the answer by beginning with a part of the problem that they did know. The work of these students illustrates an important property linking multiplication and addition, the distributive property. Written in general and formal algebraic terms, the distributive property is expressed as follows:

$$(a + b) \times c = (a \times c) + (b \times c)$$

In this vignette, there are two instances of this property. In each example, 12 is split into the two parts, *a* and *b,* and then each part is multiplied by *c*—in this case 9—to solve the problem.

Enrique's way: $12 \times 9 = (10 + 2) \times 9 = (10 \times 9) + (2 \times 9)$

Helena's way: $12 \times 9 = (6 + 6) \times 9 = (6 \times 9) + (6 \times 9)$

This unit lays the foundation for understanding the distributive property by strengthening the students' use of models for multiplication.

Enrique: Picture 12 students that each need 9 sheets of paper. 10×9 means ten of the students will need 90 sheets of paper. There are still two more students, so they need 2×9, or 18 sheets. $90 + 18$ is 108.

Helena: I drew a diagram. First I made a rectangle that is 6 by 9, and that is 54. Then I did another rectangle to make it 12×9, and so it is $54 + 54 = 108$.

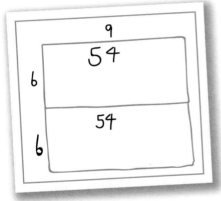

Sample Student Work

In this vignette, Enrique creates a story context to explain how his method works; Helena uses a diagram. They might have used other representations of multiplication as well, such as drawing a schematic of equal-sized groups, demonstrating with skip counting on a number line, or building stacks with cubes.

When such representations are shared, students should be encouraged to explain the connections among the diagram or cube arrangements, the story context, and the arithmetic expressions to help them articulate their reasoning. "Where in the diagram do you see (6×9)? . . . What in the story problem matches with this rectangle? . . . What arithmetic expression matches what you see here?"

Even though students are building models based on specific examples, they are forming connections between these models and the operation of multiplication. In this unit, students will use such thinking to help them figure out the combinations they have yet to learn, and to solve array problems with missing sections.

Finding Factors

In this unit, students will examine the following question: If a number is a factor of a given number, are all of the factors of the first number also factors of the given number?

Consider this vignette:

Bill, Yuki, and Anna are using skip counting to find all the factors of 24.

Bill: 6 is a factor because . . . 6, 12, 18, 24. You can get to 24 by 6s.

Yuki: I did it for 3.   3, 6, 9, 12, 15, 18, 21, 24. 3 is a factor, too.

Anna: Look, all of Bill's numbers are in Yuki's list.

Teacher: Tell me more about that. What does this mean?

Anna: If you can count by 6s to 24, you can also count by 3s to get to 24.

Bill: So if 6 is a factor of 24, 3 has to be a factor of 24, too.

Teacher: So you have found something out about 3, 6, and 24. Can you think of a way to show how you know that has to be true?

Bill, Yuki, and Anna work with cubes and then explain what they made.

Bill: We found that 6 is a factor of 24. You can see that with the cubes. We took 24 cubes and made them into stacks of 6.

Yuki: You can also see that 3 is a factor, because 3 is a factor of 6.

While Yuki talks, Bill breaks one of the six-sticks into two 3s.

Anna: What they were saying, I think, is that if you could split one of the 6s into 3s, you could split all of the 6s into 3s, and that would mean you could split the 24 into 3s.

Bill, Yuki, and Anna are using the arrangement of cubes to make the argument that if one number (6) is a factor of another (24), then factors of the first number are also factors of the second. We could summarize this idea by saying that if a is a factor of b, and b is a factor of c, then a is also a factor of c (if 3 is a factor of 6, and 6 is a factor of 24, then 3 is also a factor of 24). Even though their cube arrangement is based on specific numbers, their reasoning is not dependent on the particulars but can be extended. When such arguments are offered, challenge students to consider how the reasoning applies to additional cases: How could this argument be modified to apply to other factors of 6? Are all factors of 6 also factors of 24? Are all factors of 16 also factors of 48? By examining such questions and making arguments based on models, students are building their reasoning skills, as well as extending their knowledge of factors.

Note: *In the text for the sessions, you will find Algebra Notes that identify where these early algebra discussions are likely to arise. Some of the **Teacher Notes** and **Dialogue Boxes** further elaborate the ideas and illustrate students' conversations about them.*

Ten-Minute Math

IN THIS UNIT

Ten-Minute Math offers practice and review of key concepts for this grade level. These daily activities, to be done in ten minutes outside of math class, are introduced in a unit and repeated throughout the grade. Specific directions for the day's activity are provided in each session. For the full description and variations of each classroom activity, see *Implementing Investigations in Grade 4*.

Activity	Introduced	Full Description of Activity and Its Variations
Today's Number	Unit 1: Session 1.1 (this unit)	*Implementing Investigations in Grade 4*
Quick Images	Unit 1: Session 2.1 (this unit)	*Implementing Investigations in Grade 4*
Counting Around the Class	Unit 1: Session 3.1 (this unit)	*Implementing Investigations in Grade 4*

Today's Number

Students write several different expressions that equal a given number up to 800. They work with constraints that define the operations (addition and subtraction) and the number relationships they can use, in order to practice and develop flexibility with computation skills.

Math Focus Points

◆ Generating equivalent expressions for a number using particular constraints

◆ Practicing computation skills

◆ Using notation to record expressions

Quick Images

Students visualize and analyze images of dot patterns. After briefly viewing an image, students determine the number of dots in a pattern and write an equation to represent how they organized their count.

Math Focus Points

◆ Organizing and analyzing visual images

◆ Writing equations to represent the total number of dots in a pattern

Counting Around the Class

Students count around the class by a given number. Before the count starts, they estimate the ending number of the count and the number the last person in the class will say. Students discuss relationships between the chosen factor and its multiples and equations to represent them.

Math Focus Points

◆ Finding the multiples of numbers through skip counting

◆ Becoming familiar with multiplication patterns

◆ Understanding the relationship between skip counting and multiplication

Practice and Review

IN THIS UNIT

Practice and review play a critical role in the *Investigations* program. The following components and features are available to provide regular reinforcement of key mathematical concepts and procedures.

Books	Features	In This Unit . . .
Curriculum Unit	**Ten-Minute Math** offers practice and review of key concepts for this grade level. These daily activities, to be done in ten minutes outside of math class, are introduced in a unit and repeated throughout the grade. Specific directions for the day's activity are provided in each session. For the full description and variations of each classroom activity, see *Implementing Investigations in Grade 4*.	• **All sessions**
Student Activity Book	**Daily Practice** pages in the *Student Activity Book* provide one of three types of written practice: **reinforcement** of the content of the unit, **ongoing review,** or **enrichment** opportunities. Some Daily Practice pages will also have Ongoing Review items with multiple-choice problems similar to those on standardized tests.	• **All sessions**
	Homework pages in the *Student Activity Book* are an extension of the work done in class. At times they help students prepare for upcoming activities.	• **Session 1.1** • **Session 2.4** • **Session 1.3** • **Session 2.5** • **Session 1.5** • **Session 3.1** • **Session 2.2** • **Session 3.2** • **Session 2.3** • **Session 3.3**
Student Math Handbook	**Math Words and Ideas** in the *Student Math Handbook* are pages that summarize key words and ideas. Most Words and Ideas pages have at least one exercise.	• **Student Math Handbook, pp. 16–25, 26–34, 37–38**
	Games pages are found in a section of the *Student Math Handbook*.	• **Student Math Handbook, pp. G6, G9**

Supporting the Range of Learners

Sessions	1.1	1.2	1.4	1.5	2.1	2.2	2.3	2.5	3.1	3.2	3.3
Intervention	•	•	•	•		•	•	•	•	•	•
Extension		•							•	•	•
ELL	•		•		•	•				•	

Intervention

Suggestions are made to support and engage students who are having difficulty with a particular idea, activity, or problem.

Extension

Suggestions are made to support and engage students who finish early or may be ready for additional challenge.

English Language Learners (ELL)

As English Language Learners work through *Factors, Multiples, and Arrays,* the challenge for them will be understanding and expressing themselves during discussions about factors and about strategies for figuring out multiplication combinations. The visual array model will be an important tool for helping these students make sense of multiplication.

Encourage English Language Learners to exchange ideas with you and with smaller groups of students. Some will feel more comfortable writing down their words before being asked to say them aloud. Others might need you to provide the language for what they are doing. "I see you've taken the cubes and made an *array* of 9 × 7. Your array has nine *rows* with seven cubes in each *row*." Then ask the student to restate what you've said or to explain the next problem: "What will you do for this one? Yes, you can use your cubes to make an *array* of six *rows* with seven cubes in each *row*."

For relating multiplication situations to story contexts, students may need to draw their story idea first and then get help putting it into words. For pages of story problems, recognize that English Language Learners may understand the math but have difficulty with the language of the story. Help them by reading problems aloud, sketching objects, and modeling actions as needed.

Working with the Range of Learners: Classroom Cases is a set of episodes written by teachers that focuses on meeting the needs of the range of learners in the classroom. In the first section, *Setting up the Mathematical Community,* teachers write about how they create a supportive and productive learning environment in their classrooms. In the next section, *Accommodations for Learning,* teachers focus on specific modifications they make to meet the needs of some of their learners. In the last section, *Language and Representation,* teachers share how they help students use representations and develop language to investigate and express mathematical ideas. The questions at the end of each case provide a starting point for your own reflection or for discussion with colleagues. See *Implementing Investigations in Grade 4* for this set of episodes.

Mathematical Emphases

Whole Number Operations Understanding and working with an array model of multiplication

Math Focus Points

◆ Using arrays to model multiplication situations

◆ Breaking an array into parts to find the product represented by the array

◆ Using arrays to find factors of 2-digit numbers

◆ Identifying features of numbers, including prime, square, and composite numbers

Whole Number Operations Reasoning about numbers and their factors

Math Focus Points

◆ Finding the multiples of a number by skip counting

Computational Fluency Fluency with multiplication combinations to 12×12

Math Focus Points

◆ Identifying and learning multiplication combinations not yet known fluently

◆ Using known multiplication combinations to determine the products of more difficult combinations

Representing Multiplication with Arrays

SESSION 1.1	p. 26	Student Activity Book	Student Math Handbook	Professional Development: Read Ahead of Time	
Things That Come in Arrays Students consider how examples of arrays from the real world represent multiplication. They develop and share strategies for finding the product represented by an array.		1–4	16–19	• **Mathematics in This Unit**, p. 10 • **Teacher Notes:** Images of Multiplication, p. 115; Representing Multiplication with Arrays, p. 117 • **Dialogue Box:** How Many In This Array?, p. 128 • **Part 4: Ten-Minute Math** in *Implementing Investigations in Grade 4:* Today's Number	
SESSION 1.2 p. 32					
Making Arrays Students use what they know about multiplication to find all the arrays for given numbers.		5	23		
SESSION 1.3 p. 38					
Making Arrays, *continued* Students continue to use what they know about multiplication to find all the arrays for given numbers. They discuss special features of some numbers, including prime and square numbers.		6–8	18–19, 27–28		

Materials to Gather	Materials to Prepare
• **T1, Things That Come in Arrays** • **Color tiles or connecting cubes** (as needed)	• **M1, Things That Come in Arrays** Make copies. (as needed) • **M2, Centimeter Grid Paper** Make copies. (as needed) • **M3–M4, Family Letter** Make copies. (1 per student)
• **T1, Things That Come in Arrays** (See Session 1.1) • **T2, Centimeter Grid Paper** • **Overhead color tiles** (optional) • **Color tiles or connecting cubes** (as needed) • **12˝ x 18˝ construction paper** (2 sheets per pair, plus extras) • **Scissors** (1 per pair) • **Glue sticks** (1 per pair) • **Markers** (1 per pair)	• **M2, Centimeter Grid Paper** Make copies. (1–2 sheets per pair, plus extras as needed) • **M5–M6, Family Letter** Make copies. (1 per student)
• **Students' "Ways to Make [24]" posters** (See Session 1.2) • **Materials for Making Arrays** See Session 1.2.	• **M7–M8, Family Letter** Make copies. (1 per student)

Overhead Transparency

Representing Multiplication with Arrays, *continued*

	Student Activity Book	Student Math Handbook	Professional Development: Read Ahead of Time	
SESSION 1.4 p. 42				
Which Combinations Do I Know? In the array card game *Factor Pairs,* students build on known multiplication combinations to find the products of more difficult combinations to 12 ×12.	9–10	22; G6	• **Teacher Note:** Learning and Assessing Multiplication Combinations, p. 120 • **Dialogue Box:** Another Array Picture, p. 129	
SESSION 1.5 p. 47				
Using Arrays to Multiply Through playing *Factor Pairs* and solving array problems, students continue to use arrays to visualize how to build on the multiplication combinations they know to learn the hardest combinations.	11–14	22	• **Part 2: Using *Investigations*** in *Implementing Investigations in Grade 4:* The Curriculum Units	

Materials to Gather	Materials to Prepare
	• **T5, T15, T18, T23, Array Cards** Cut out selected cards (7×8, 8×11, 6×10, and 9×12) as examples for classroom discussion. • **M9–M29, Array Cards** If you are not using manufactured Array Cards, make copies on card stock and cut out the arrays. Write the product on the back of each card. Also write one of the dimensions of the array, using smaller numbers, along one side of the cards (sometimes the longer dimension, sometimes the shorter). Enlist the help of aides, parent volunteers, or students. (1 set per pair) • **M30,** *Factor Pairs* Make copies. (as needed)
• **Array Cards** (1 set per pair; from Session 1.4) • **Connecting cubes or color tiles** (as needed) • **Students' "Combinations I Know/Combinations I'm Working On" lists** (from Session 1.4)	• **M2, Centimeter Grid Paper** Make copies. (as needed) • **M31, Assessment: Representing** 8×6 Make copies. (1 per student) • **M32, Assessment Checklist: Representing** 8×6 ☑ Make copies. (1–2 for teacher use, as needed)

☑ Checklist Available

Things That Come in Arrays

Math Focus Points

◆ Using arrays to model multiplication situations

◆ Breaking an array into parts to find the product represented by the array

◆ Finding the multiples of a number by skip counting

Vocabulary

multiplication
array
dimension

Today's Plan		Materials
DISCUSSION **❶ How Many in This Array?**	20 MIN · CLASS · PAIRS	• *Student Activity Book*, p. 1
ACTIVITY **❷ Things That Come in Arrays**	40 MIN · CLASS · PAIRS	• *Student Activity Book*, p. 2 • M1*; M2* • T1 • Color tiles; connecting cubes
SESSION FOLLOW-UP **❸ Daily Practice and Homework**		• *Student Activity Book*, pp. 3–4 • *Student Math Handbook*, pp. 16–19 • M3–M4, Family Letter*

*See *Materials to Prepare*, p. 23.

Ten-Minute Math

Note: The Ten-Minute Math activity for this investigation, *Today's Number,* is not formally introduced in this unit. For a full description of the activity, see **Part 4: Ten-Minute Math** in *Implementing Investigations in Grade 4: Today's Number*

Today's Number Students create expressions that equal 425. They must use one combination that adds up to 100 in each expression. For example: $15 + 85 + 300 + 25 = 425$ and $\underline{39 + 61} + 250 + 75 = 425$. Collect a few expressions to write on the board.

Which numbers in your expression equal 100 when added together? Are you sure the whole expression equals 425?

DISCUSSION
How Many in This Array?

20 MIN CLASS PAIRS

Professional Development

❶ **Teacher Note:** Images of Multiplication, p. 115

❷ **Dialogue Box:** How Many in This Array?, p. 128

Math Focus Points for Discussion

◆ Breaking an array into parts to find the product represented by the array

◆ Finding the multiples of a number by skip counting

Begin by telling students that their first topic of study in mathematics this year will be multiplication.

Tell pairs of students to turn to *Student Activity Book* page 1.

This page has a picture of a case of juice cans, but the delivery person has left a baseball cap on top. How can we figure out how many cans of juice are in this case, including the ones that we can't see?

Give students time to solve the problem in pairs. Then bring them back together to discuss how they found their solutions.❶

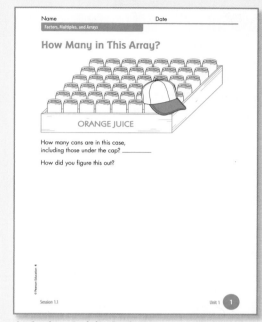

▲ Student Activity Book, p. 1

Students use the structure of an array to determine the total number of items in that array.

Possible strategies students may have used include these:❷

• Finding the number of cans in half of the array and doubling that number

• Skip counting by one of the factors

• Reasoning from known multiplication combinations

Professional Development

③ Teacher Note: Representing Multiplication with Arrays, p. 117

Teaching Notes

④ Describing Arrays Students may describe this array as either three rows of two cans or two rows of three cans. When students write a multiplication expression for an array, what is important is that they can explain what each number means. For example, one student might show how 3×2 represents 3 rows of cans with 2 in each row, and another student might show how the same expression represents 3 cans in each of 2 rows.

⑤ Mathematical Vocabulary Introduce mathematical vocabulary by using terms yourself as they arise in the context of mathematical work. If the introduction of mathematical terms is accompanied by activities that make their meanings clear, students will begin using these terms naturally as they hear them used repeatedly in meaningful contexts.

▲ Student Activity Book, p. 2;
Resource Masters, M1; T1 PORTFOLIO

ACTIVITY

② Things That Come in Arrays

40 MIN   CLASS   PAIRS

Remind students that when they worked on multiplication in Grade 3, they often spent time working with objects in a rectangular arrangement of equal rows of objects called an array. ③

Groups of things often come in rectangular arrays. Imagine a six-pack of juice cans. How many rows do you see? How many cans are in each row? Does anyone see it differently? ④

Draw students' attention to the transparency of Things That Come in Arrays (T1).

What other things can you think of that come in rectangular arrays? Think about the way food is packaged at the grocery store. What things in this room are in arrays?

Write down a few of the students' ideas (e.g., windowpanes, cubbies, dot stickers, or groupings of desks) on the transparency. Begin to use the term **dimensions** to identify the number of rows and columns in the array so that students become used to hearing this language. ⑤

Helena, you noticed that our cubbies are an array of 4 × 3. One dimension, the number of cubbies in each row, is 4, and the other dimension, the number of rows, is 3. How could I write that as a multiplication expression?

Choose one or two items on the list, and ask questions to help students connect the number of rows and columns in an array to the idea of multiplication as groups of things. Use one of the arrays that students found in the classroom.

- Look at this array of [desks]. Can you use multiplication to describe this array?

- Remember that multiplication is about groups of things. If we think of a row in this array as a group, how many groups are there?

- How many [desks] are in each group?

- What are some ways that we can find how many [desks] are in this 4-by-6 array without counting each [desk]?

What Is It?	How Many in the Array?	Dimensions	Drawing in the Array
classroom cubbies	12	3 rows of 4 4 rows of 3 3 × 4 4 × 3	
carton of eggs	12	2 rows of 6 6 rows of 2 2 × 6 6 × 2	
sheet of dot stickers	32	4 rows of 8 8 rows of 4 4 × 8 8 × 4	

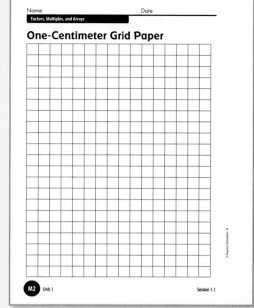

One-Centimeter Grid Paper

▲ Resource Masters, M2; T2

Record some students' suggestions. Possible strategies include these:

- Skip counting (4, 8, 12, 16, 20, 24)

- Thinking 2 × 6 = 12 and doubling to get 4 × 6 = 24

- Using a known multiplication combination (6 × 4 = 24)

Students work in pairs to think of other things that come in arrays and then record and describe their arrays on *Student Activity Book* page 2. Students may need more than one sheet, so have extra copies of Things That Come in Arrays (M1) on hand. Students may use color tiles, connecting cubes, or Centimeter Grid Paper (M2) to represent the arrays they come up with.

Before the session ends, bring the class back together with their work. Let students know that they will have a chance to add to their charts later in class. For now, ask students to name and describe some of the arrays they came up with. Add the new examples to the class list on Things That Come in Arrays (T1).

ONGOING ASSESSMENT: Observing Students at Work

Students generate examples of arrays of familiar objects and find the products represented by these arrays.

- **Do students think of arrays with products greater than 12?** Greater than 24?

- **How are students determining the number of items in their arrays?** Do they use skip counting?

- **Do students use multiplication combinations they already know to help them find the product of an array?** For example, when figuring out the product of a 4×8 array, do they use $2 \times 8 = 16$ and then double that amount?

DIFFERENTIATION: Supporting the Range of Learners

Intervention Using materials such as color tiles or connecting cubes to represent arrays, helps many students visualize the relationship between the two dimensions in an array model of multiplication. Students may use tiles or cubes to copy an array that they see in the classroom, such as the panes on a window or the tiles on the ceiling. They may also imagine an array that they are familiar with, such as an egg carton, and construct that with tiles or cubes.

Students may use tiles or cubes to construct an array.

Ask students to tell you about the arrays that they make, asking questions such as these:

- How many rows does your array have?

- Where are the rows in your tile construction?

- How many tiles are in each row? Can you point them out to me?

- You've made an array that has [6] rows with [4] tiles in each row. How many tiles are there in your whole array? How could you write that as a multiplication equation?

Drawing arrays on Centimeter Grid Paper (M2), with squares that can be counted, may be helpful to some students. Model this yourself, and then ask students to draw some arrays of their own. Make extra copies (M2) available to students who want to draw their arrays on grid paper rather than in the limited space allotted on *Student Activity Book* page 2.

ELL Have pictures of common grocery store arrays on hand, or create labels to place on classroom items in arrays. In class discussion, refer to the labeled items to reinforce the vocabulary. When students are asked to write a story for a multiplication combination on the End-of-Unit Assessment, English Language Learners can refer to these labeled items.

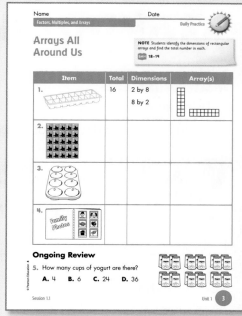

▲ **Student Activity Book, p. 3**

SESSION FOLLOW-UP

3 Daily Practice and Homework

 Daily Practice: For reinforcement of this unit's content, have students complete *Student Activity Book* page 3.

 Homework: Ask students to look for arrays at home. Have students record and describe the arrays they find on *Student Activity Book* page 4. When students arrive at school in the morning, you may ask them to name some of the things that come in arrays that they discovered at home and add these items to the class's list on the transparency.

 Student Math Handbook: Students and families may use *Student Math Handbook* pages 16–19 for reference and review. See pages 134–139 in the back of this unit.

 Family Letter: Send home copies of the Family Letter (M3–M4).

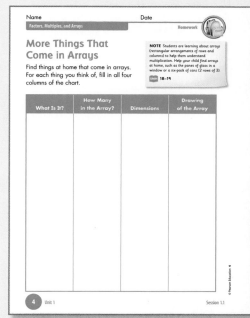

▲ **Student Activity Book, p. 4**

Making Arrays

Math Focus Points

◆ Using arrays to model multiplication situations

◆ Using arrays to find factors of 2-digit numbers

Vocabulary

factor

Today's Plan		Materials
ACTIVITY **① Introducing Making Arrays**	15 MIN CLASS	• T1 (from Session 1.1); T2 • Connecting cubes or color tiles; overhead color tiles (optional)
ACTIVITY **② Making Arrays**	45 MIN PAIRS	• M2* • 12″ x 18″ construction paper; scissors; glue sticks; markers; connecting cubes; color tiles
SESSION FOLLOW-UP **③ Daily Practice**		• *Student Activity Book,* p. 5 • *Student Math Handbook,* p. 23 • M5–M6, Family Letter*

*See *Materials to Prepare,* p. 23.

Ten-Minute Math

Today's Number Students form expressions that equal 219. They must use only subtraction in each expression. For example: $239 - 20 = 219$ and $250 - 30 - 1 = 219$. Collect a few expressions to write on the board. Ask students to share their strategies for writing each expression and tell how they know their expression equals 219.

ACTIVITY

Introducing Making Arrays

15 MIN   CLASS

From the items the class compiled for the transparency of Things That Come in Arrays (T1) in Session 1.1, choose an array that is familiar to all students, such as a 6 × 2 array of 12 eggs. Students will each need the same number of color tiles or connecting cubes.

What other ways can you think of to arrange 12 eggs into an array, besides 6 by 2?

Students work on this individually for a few minutes and then share their solutions. If you have overhead color tiles, you may model students' ideas on the overhead. Then, on a transparency of Centimeter Grid Paper (T2), draw the arrays that students suggest. Ask students how to label these with their dimensions and how to write a multiplication expression for each array.

1 × 12   12 × 1

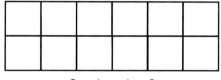

2 × 6   6 × 2

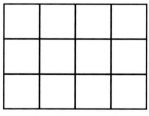

3 × 4   4 × 3

When students cannot think of any more arrays for 12, make a list of the dimensions of the arrays:

3 × 4   2 × 6   1 × 12

4 × 3   6 × 2   12 × 1

Each of the dimensions on this list is a factor of 12. That means 12 can be divided by each of these numbers with no leftovers. What are all the factors of 12?

Teaching Note

❶ **Factors and Array Dimensions** Although students learned and used the term *factor* in Grade 3, it is likely that many will need to revisit its meaning. When we talk about the size of an array, we say that the *dimensions* of the array are "2 by 6" or "6 by 2." These dimensions can also be written as a multiplication expression: 2 × 6 or 6 × 2. As a visual model of multiplication, arrays help students see the relationship between the dimensions (the number of rows and the number in each row) and the number of items in the array. The dimensions, then, are also the factors in a multiplication equation.

Teaching Note

❷ **Factors of a Number and Its Multiples** The purpose of pairing numbers in this way is so that students have an opportunity to use what they find out about the arrays of one number to help them find the arrays of the other (which in every case is a multiple of the first number). This idea, that the factors of a number are also factors of its multiples, will be a focus for further investigation and discussion in Investigation 3. For now, the opportunity is provided for students to begin to notice this relationship and see how it helps them solve the problem of identifying the factors of a number.

As students identify the factors of 12, list them in order (1, 2, 3, 4, 6, 12). Then ask students to identify the pairs of factors that go together to make 12. Draw lines to connect the factor pairs, a visual that some students may find helpful.

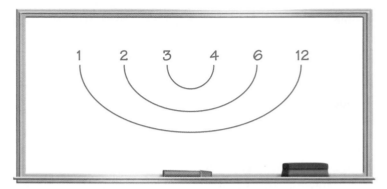

Ask students whether they notice any arrays that have identical factors such as 3 × 4 and 4 × 3. Point out that 3 and 4 are both factors of 12 and that you can turn one array to look exactly like the other. When students find arrays, it is only necessary to identify one array (3 × 4), and it is understood that the array can be turned to look like 4 × 3.

ACTIVITY

❷ Making Arrays

45 MIN   PAIRS

Students work with a partner to find all the arrays for a related pair of numbers.❷ You may assign one of the number pairs below to each pair of students or write the pairs on the board and let partners choose the number pair they would like. However, make sure that each number pair is used by only one pair of students, if possible.

15 and 45	23 and 46
16 and 64	24 and 48
17 and 34	25 and 50
18 and 54	27 and 81
19 and 38	29 and 58
21 and 42	36 and 72
22 and 66	

Hand out copies of Centimeter Grid Paper (M2), scissors, glue sticks, and construction paper. Students may also use color tiles or connecting cubes to help them plan their arrays. They find all the possible arrays for each of their numbers and cut out each array from the grid paper. They glue the arrays onto a sheet of 12″ x 18″ construction paper to create a poster for each number, with a title such as "Ways to Make 24." Students label each array with its dimensions (for example, 6 × 4 and 4 × 6) written as multiplication expressions.

About 20 minutes into this activity, stop for a short discussion about how students know when they have found all of the arrays for a given number. Ask a pair of students who have completed the arrays for one of their numbers to talk about how they know they are finished. For example, you might ask the following questions:

- What are the smallest and largest factors that you found for your number? Could there be anything smaller? Larger?

- Were there numbers that you knew wouldn't work? Why?

- Why are there no factors between [half of the number] and [the number itself] (e.g., between 12 and 24 or 18 and 36)?

Keep this discussion short for now because students will come back to these ideas in a later session.❸

Students make arrays for given numbers and label them with their dimensions.

At the end of the allotted time, let students know that they will continue working on their array posters in the next session. Have students save their posters and materials for use in Session 1.3.

Algebra Note

❸ **Properties of Factors** As they work on this activity, some students might notice number relationships such as these:

- All the factors of the smaller number are also factors of the larger number.
- If 5 is not a factor of the larger number, then 10 cannot be a factor either.

Encourage students to articulate such ideas in their own words.

ONGOING ASSESSMENT: Observing Students at Work

Students use what they know about multiplication to find all the arrays for a given number and label the dimensions of each array.

- **How are students using multiplication combinations they know to generate additional arrays?** (*"2 × 24 works for 48, so what if we double the 2? 4 works for 40, so it has to work for 48 because 48 is just two more 4s."*)

- **Are students finding all the possible arrays for their numbers, or leaving some out?** How are they determining if they have them all?

- **How are students making sure that the product is accurate?**

When students think they are finished even though they have not found all the arrays for their number, you might ask:

- Can you see any way that you can cut either of these arrays and make a new array?

- If 2 is a factor and 6 is a factor, could there be anything between 2 and 6?

- Did you check all the numbers between 2 and 10? Five couldn't work because 42 isn't a multiple of 5. What about 3 and 4?

DIFFERENTIATION: Supporting the Range of Learners

Intervention Pull together a small group of students who need help getting started. Work together as a group to find the arrays for a smaller number, such as 20. Have color tiles or connecting cubes on hand for students to construct the arrays, and rearrange the manipulatives to make arrays of different dimensions. Ask questions such as these:

- What are some ways you can think of to break this number apart?

- Can we make an array that will have two equal rows?

Extension For students who can easily find all the arrays for numbers such as 36 and 48, suggest larger numbers that are related to the numbers students worked on (such as 150 if they worked on 50, or 108 if they worked on 72). You may also ask them to choose one or two numbers that they think might have many different arrays. They can record these on Centimeter Grid Paper (M2). For students who want to pursue these ideas further, you could pose this problem: What 2-digit number has the largest number of arrays?

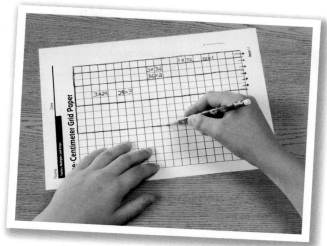

A student who easily made arrays for 36 might then work on arrays for 72.

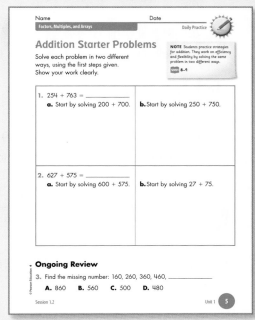

▲ **Student Activity Book, p. 5**

---

3 SESSION FOLLOW-UP
Daily Practice

 Daily Practice: For ongoing review, have students complete *Student Activity Book* page 5.

 Student Math Handbook: Students and families may use *Student Math Handbook* page 23 for reference and review. See pages 134–139 in the back of this unit.

 Family Letter: Send home copies of Family Letter (M5–M6).

Making Arrays, *continued*

Math Focus Points

◆ Using arrays to model multiplication situations

◆ Using arrays to find factors of 2-digit numbers

◆ Identifying features of numbers, including prime, square, and composite numbers

Vocabulary

prime number
composite number
square number

Today's Plan		Materials
ACTIVITY **① Making Arrays,** *continued*	🕐 30 MIN 👥 PAIRS	• M2* • Students' "Ways to Make [24]" posters (from Session 1.2) • Materials for Making Arrays from Session 1.2, p. 32
ACTIVITY **② Looking at Our Arrays**	🕐 15 MIN 👥 PAIRS	• *Student Activity Book,* p. 6
DISCUSSION **③ What Do You Notice About Arrays?**	🕐 15 MIN 👥 CLASS	• *Student Activity Book,* p. 6
SESSION FOLLOW-UP **④ Daily Practice and Homework**		• *Student Activity Book,* pp. 7–8 • *Student Math Handbook,* pp. 18–19, 27–28 • M7–M8, Family Letter*

*See *Materials to Prepare,* p. 23.

Ten-Minute Math

Today's Number Students create expressions that equal 562 using addition. They must use multiples of 10 in each expression. For example: $562 = 500 + 50 + 10 + 2$ and $80 + 20 + 450 + 12 = 562$. Collect a few expressions to write on the board.

How do you know this expression equals 562?

How did you combine the multiples of 10?

ACTIVITY

Making Arrays, *continued*

30 MIN   PAIRS

Student pairs resume work on finding all possible arrays for the numbers they were assigned in Session 1.2.

As students finish a number, post their work in the classroom so that it can be easily seen. In the next activity, students examine these posters in preparation for a discussion about features of the arrays they have made. Students may have time to work on more than one pair of numbers.

Refer to Session 1.2, pages 36–37, for suggestions for Ongoing Assessment and Differentiation.

ACTIVITY

Looking at Our Arrays

15 MIN   PAIRS

When pairs of students are ready, have them spend a few minutes examining the class's array posters and answering questions about them on *Student Activity Book* page 6.

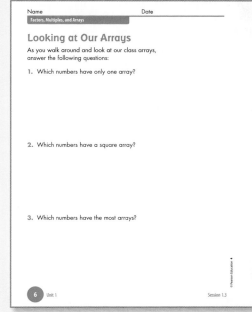

▲ **Student Activity Book, p. 6**

Students examine their classmates' posters to find which numbers have only one array, which have square arrays, and which have the most arrays.

Math Notes

❶ **Array Dimensions** For the purposes of this discussion, arrays with the same dimensions no matter what their orientation are considered the same (e.g., a 1 × 17 and a 17 × 1 grid).

❷ **The Number 1** The number 1 has only one factor. It is a unique number that is neither prime nor composite.

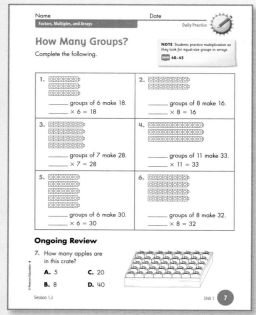

▲ Student Activity Book, p. 7

15 MIN   CLASS

DISCUSSION

③ What Do You Notice About Arrays?

Math Focus Points for Discussion

◆ Identifying features of numbers, including prime, square, and composite numbers

Bring the class back together to share what they found out. List students' answers to the questions on *Student Activity Book* page 6. Ideas that should emerge from this discussion include the following:

• **17, 19, 23, and 29** have only **one possible array.**❶ Ask students to think about how many factors these numbers have. Tell students that these numbers with exactly two factors—1 and the number itself—are called prime numbers. Numbers having more than one array, or more than two factors, are called composite numbers.❷ Students might notice that all the prime numbers are odd except 2.

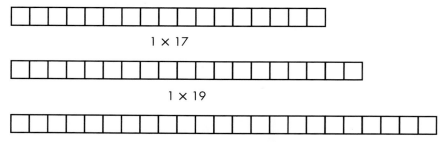

• **16, 25, 36, and 49** each have a **square array.** In order to be a square, an array must have the same number for both dimensions; for example a 6 × 6 array. Tell students that numbers that can be represented by a square array are called square numbers. Ask students to name some more square numbers and to explain how they know that these are square. Draw these square arrays with their factors and the product. (You do not need to draw the inside grid.) Students can add these numbers to their lists of square numbers.

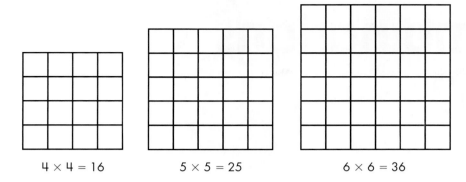

$4 \times 4 = 16$ $5 \times 5 = 25$ $6 \times 6 = 36$

- **24, 30, 36, 45, and 48** have **many arrays.** Ask students what they notice about numbers that have many arrays and numbers that have only a few. Students may notice that not all larger numbers have more arrays than smaller numbers.❸

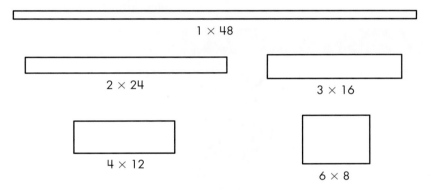

1×48

2×24

3×16

4×12

6×8

Math Note

❸ **Common Factors of Multiples** Students may have other observations to make about their work, particularly about the relationship between the numbers in the pair they worked on. They may notice that both numbers had factors in common or that one number had an array that was twice (or three times) the size of the other number. These relationships will be discussed more in Investigation 3.

▲ **Student Activity Book, p. 8**

 SESSION FOLLOW-UP

4 Daily Practice and Homework

 Daily Practice: For reinforcement of this unit's content, have students complete *Student Activity Book* page 7.

 Homework: On *Student Activity Book* page 8, students solve three related story problems involving multiplication.

 Student Math Handbook: Students and families may use *Student Math Handbook* pages 18–19, 27–28 for reference and review. See pages 134–139 in the back of this unit.

Family Letter: Send home copies of the Family Letter (M7–M8).

Which Combinations Do I Know?

Math Focus Points

◆ Identifying and learning multiplication combinations not yet known fluently

◆ Using known multiplication combinations to determine the products of more difficult combinations

◆ Breaking an array into parts to find the product represented by the array

Vocabulary

multiplication combination

Today's Plan			Materials
ACTIVITY **①Array Cards**	🕐 15 MIN	👥 CLASS	• Transparent examples of Array Cards*
ACTIVITY **②Factor Pairs**	🕐 30 MIN	👥 PAIRS	• M9–M29*; M30*
DISCUSSION **③Another Array Picture**	🕐 15 MIN	👥 CLASS	• *Student Activity Book*, p. 9
SESSION FOLLOW-UP **④Daily Practice**			• *Student Activity Book*, p. 10 • *Student Math Handbook*, pp. 22; G6

*See *Materials to Prepare*, p. 25.

Ten-Minute Math

Today's Number Students write expressions that equal 471 and that use addition and subtraction. For example: 471 = 600 − 200 + 50 + 30 − 9 and 300 + 150 + 21 = 471. Collect expressions that include different-sized numbers and are of different lengths. Look for ones that use only addition, only subtraction, and a combination of both.

How can you be sure that this expression equals 471?

Explain your strategy so that the rest of us can understand it.

ACTIVITY

Array Cards

15 MIN   CLASS

Display four transparent Array Cards such as 7 × 8, 6 × 10, 8 × 11, and 9 × 12 (T5, T15, T18, and T23) on the overhead.

Tell students that the arrays you are showing them come from a set of Array Cards that are the same as those that they used in Grade 3 for playing games and practicing multiplication combinations. However, the fourth grade set includes arrays with products that are greater than 50, up to 144 (12 × 12). Ask students to think about how they would find the products represented by these four arrays.❶ ❷

Are there any here that seem easier than others? What do you already know about these numbers that could help you figure out how many squares are in each of these arrays?

Take suggestions from students, which are likely to include the following:

• Skip counting

• Remembering patterns for multiplying with 10 and 11

• "Just knowing"

• Reasoning from known multiplication combinations

Students might say:

"I know that 3 × 12 is 36, so 9 × 12 would be three of those."

"I know that 9 × 10 = 90, and 9 × 2 = 18, so 9 × 12 = 108."

As students share strategies that use known multiplication combinations, ask them to come up and demonstrate where the smaller arrays are located within the larger arrays.

Anna, you said that you used the factor pair 3 × 12 = 36 to help you figure out the product for the 9 × 12 array. Could you show us on the overhead where you see a 3 × 12 array within the 9 × 12 array?

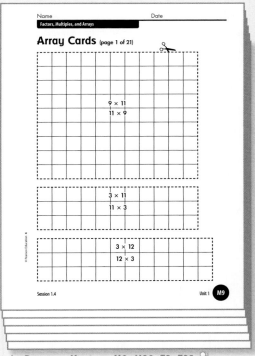

▲ Resource Masters, M9–M29; T3–T23

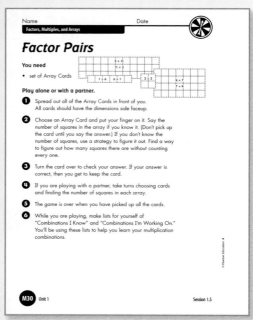

▲ Resource Masters, M30

[Alejandro], you used $9 \times 10 = 90$ and $9 \times 2 = 18$ to find the product for the 9×12 array. Can you show us those smaller arrays within the 9×12 array?

ACTIVITY

2 Factor Pairs

30 MIN   PAIRS

The game *Factor Pairs* will be familiar to students who played it in Grade 3, when they worked with multiplication combinations with products up to 50. In this version, they work with combinations that have products up to 12×12.

Today you're going to play a game called *Factor Pairs* with Array Cards.

Spread out a deck of Array Cards on a table, and explain that you are placing them factor side up.

Choose a volunteer to be your partner as you explain the game. Make available copies of the rules for *Factor Pairs* (M30) as needed.

The teacher plays a demonstration round of Factor Pairs *with a student. Players must figure out the product of each Array Card.*

Ask the volunteer to touch one of the cards.

Can you say the number of squares in the array? If you don't "just know" the answer, use a strategy to figure it out so that you don't have to count each square.

After the student offers an answer, turn the card over to check.❸ Explain that if the answer is correct, the student keeps the card. Otherwise, flip it back so that the factor side is up.

For my turn, I pick another card and do the same thing. Partners should keep taking turns until all the cards are picked up.

During this demonstration, discuss briefly what it means to know a multiplication combination quickly, without having to figure it out by skip counting.❹

Have students divide a blank sheet of paper into two columns, titled "Combinations I Know" and "Combinations I'm Working On." Then have pairs of students play the game. As they play, partners can help monitor each other in deciding which column a multiplication expression goes in ("Combinations I Know" or "Combinations I'm Working On"). Tell students that you expect that many of the new, bigger arrays will start out on the list of combinations they need to work on.

ONGOING ASSESSMENT: Observing Students at Work

Students use Array Cards to find the products of pairs of numbers from 1 × 2 to 12 × 12.

- **Are most students familiar, if not fluent, with multiplication combinations for products to 50?** Which combinations are still hard for some students?

- **How are students figuring out the products on the Array Cards?** Are they skip counting? Are they using other multiplication combinations that they know?

DIFFERENTIATION: Supporting the Range of Learners

Intervention Questioning students as they work can encourage them to develop more efficient strategies based on knowledge they have of multiplication relationships. Consider, for example, the Array Card for 5 × 7 (or 7 × 5).

- How will you figure out how many squares there are altogether?

- Can you skip count by 5 (or 7)? How will that help?

- Is there a multiple of 5 (or 7) that you already know that will get you partway there (for example, 2 × 5 or 5 × 5)? How can that help?

- Can you see any multiplication combinations that you know within the big array?

Differentiation

❸ **English Language Learners** If an English Language Learner is uncertain about the word name to call out for the number of squares on an Array Card, the student can write the number instead, or point it out on the number line or 100 chart.

Teaching Note

❹ **Fluency** One of the goals for this unit is for students to become fluent with the multiplication combinations to 12 × 12. Fluency means that students can quickly access the products of these combinations mentally, either because they are immediately known or because the calculation that is used is so effortless as to be essentially automatic (for example, quickly calculating the product of 8 × 7 by doubling 4 × 7).

⑤ **Dialogue Box:** Another Array Picture, p. 129

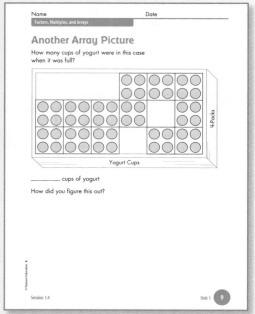

▲ Student Activity Book, p. 9

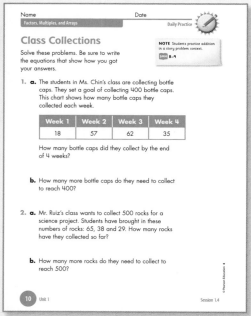

▲ Student Activity Book, p. 10

Using a familiar context, such as multiplication stories, is a way to help students visualize how arrays represent multiplication.

Let's say this array is a case of soup cans, and you need to figure out how many cans you have. How many would be in one row? How many rows are there? How many soup cans is that altogether?

DISCUSSION

③ Another Array Picture

15 MIN   CLASS

Math Focus Points for Discussion

◆ Breaking an array into parts to find the product represented by the array

Have pairs turn to *Student Activity Book* page 9.

Here's another array picture problem for you to solve. In this picture, a case of yogurt containers that come in packs of 4 has been opened, and some of the 4-packs are missing. How many yogurts were in this case to begin with?

Students work on this problem in pairs for a few minutes. Encourage students to think of efficient ways to find the number of yogurts without counting them by ones. Then gather ideas for how to solve the problem, and write them on the board or overhead.⑤

SESSION FOLLOW-UP

④ Daily Practice

 Daily Practice: For ongoing review, have students complete *Student Activity Book* page 10.

 Student Math Handbook: Students and families may use *Student Math Handbook* page 22 and G6 for reference and review. See pages 134–139 in the back of this unit.

Using Arrays to Multiply

Math Focus Points

◆ Using known multiplication combinations to determine the products of more difficult combinations

◆ Breaking an array into parts to find the product represented by the array

◆ Using arrays to model multiplication situations

Today's Plan	Materials
MATH WORKSHOP ❶ **Using Arrays to Multiply** ⓐ **Array Picture Problems** ⓑ *Factor Pairs* ⓒ **Assessment: Representing 8 × 6** ⏱ 45 MIN	ⓐ • *Student Activity Book*, pp. 11–12 • M2* (from Session 1.1) • Connecting cubes or color tiles ⓑ • M9–M29 (from Session 1.4) • Students' "Combinations" lists (from Session 1.4) ⓒ • M31*; M32* ☑
DISCUSSION ❷ **Sharing Our Work** ⏱ 15 MIN 👪 CLASS	• *Student Activity Book*, p. 11 (Problem A)
SESSION FOLLOW-UP ❸ **Daily Practice and Homework**	• *Student Activity Book*, pp. 13–14 • *Student Math Handbook*, p. 22

*See *Materials to Prepare*, p. 25.

Ten-Minute Math

Today's Number Students use at least three numbers to create expressions that equal 800. They must use both addition and subtraction in each expression. For example: $625 + 75 + 300 - 200 = 800$ and $500 + 500 - 100 - 100 = 800$. Collect a few expressions to write on the board. Ask students to explain how they know each expression equals 800.

❶ Teacher Note: Part 2: Using *Investigations* in *Implementing Investigations in Grade 4:* The Curriculum Units

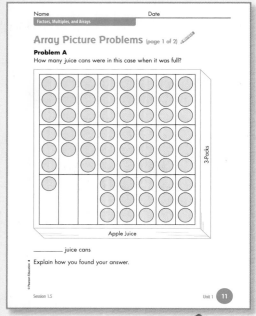

▲ **Student Activity Book, p. 11**

MATH WORKSHOP

❶ Using Arrays to Multiply

45 MIN

Although most students will be familiar with the structure of Math Workshop from previous grades, it is important to spend time in this session laying the foundations for what it means to have a productive Math Workshop time. Issues such as working cooperatively with a partner and staying focused on the mathematics of each activity are things that students often need reminders about. Because this is the first Math Workshop of the year, here are some important things to bring up:

- Where students will find the materials for the activities

- How you expect them to clean up and return materials at the end of each session

- How students will be keeping track of the work that they do

- How students will determine when to move on to a new activity

After this first experience with Math Workshop for the year, and before the next Math Workshop in Investigation 2, plan to spend some time outside math time discussing with students how it went. Questions you might ask include these:

- What helped you work independently? What made it hard?

- What helped you work cooperatively with your partner? What were the difficulties that you had to work out together?

- How did you manage your time so that you got to all the math work that you needed to get to?❶

In this Math Workshop, students work on more array picture problems like the ones they discussed in Sessions 1.1 and 1.4 and continue to play *Factor Pairs.* Students should divide their workshop time so that they get to work on both activities, as well as the assessment activity.

❶A Array Picture Problems

INDIVIDUALS

On *Student Activity Book* pages 11–12, students solve two problems about arrays and explain how they solved the problems. Encourage them to make their explanations clear enough that someone reading their work will be able to follow their thinking, including using mathematical notation and pictures if needed. Let students know that they should be sure to do Problem A on *Student Activity Book* page 11 because they will discuss this problem at the end of the session.

Solving array problems helps students develop strong visual images that support their understanding of multiplication.

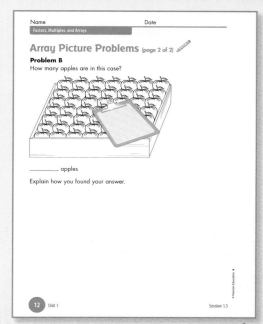

▲ Student Activity Book, p. 12

 ONGOING ASSESSMENT: Observing Students at Work

Students determine the product represented by incomplete or partially covered arrays.

- **Can students visualize what the complete array looks like?**

- **How do students solve these problems?** Do they skip count by one dimension? Do they reason from known relationships?

- **Are students' solutions accurate?**

 DIFFERENTIATION: Supporting the Range of Learners

Intervention Some students may want to reconstruct the complete arrays in these pictures with color tiles or connecting cubes or redraw them on grid paper.

 **1B** *Factor Pairs* **PAIRS**

For complete details about this activity, see Session 1.4, pages 44–45. Remind students to add to their "Combinations I Know/Combinations I'm Working On" lists as they play.

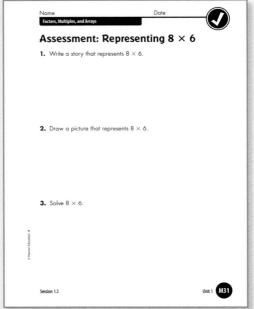

▲ Resource Masters, M31 *PORTFOLIO*

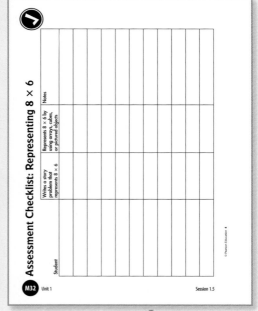

▲ Resource Masters, M32 ☑

1C Assessment: Representing 8 × 6

INDIVIDUALS

This is an observed assessment of *Benchmark 2: Use arrays, pictures or models of groups, and story contexts to represent multiplication situations.* Students work individually on a copy of Assessment: Representing 8 × 6 (M31), drawing a model and writing a story problem to represent 8 × 6, and then solving the problem.

Collect and review this work to identify any student in the class who cannot clearly and accurately identify the number of groups and the amount in each group in a multiplication expression.

Use Assessment Checklist: Representing 8 × 6 (M32) to make notes on what you observe as students work and, later, what you notice from looking at their written work.

ONGOING ASSESSMENT: Observing Students at Work

Students represent and solve a multiplication problem.

- **Can students accurately model or draw 8 × 6?** If they draw an 8 × 6 array, can they identify the groups and how many in each group? Do they know how to find the total number in the array? If they show 8 groups of 6 cubes or draw a picture of 6 groups of 8 objects, can they identify what the 8 and the 6 represent in their model or picture?

- **Can students write a story problem that represents 8 × 6?** Do they correctly represent 8 groups of 6 things or 6 groups of 8 things?

DIFFERENTIATION: Supporting the Range of Learners

Intervention Make a note of any students who cannot correctly identify 8 groups of 6 things or 6 groups of 8 things. These students need more work on representing multiplication situations. Ask them to find and draw more examples of arrays that they see in the world and to identify the number of groups and how many are in each group.

② Sharing Our Work

15 MIN **CLASS**

Math Focus Points for Discussion

◆ Using known multiplication combinations to determine the products of more difficult combinations

After every Math Workshop this year, we'll usually come back together to talk about some of the math that you worked on. Who would like to share the work you did on Array Picture Problem A?

Choose a few volunteers to share their solutions. Ask questions of the whole class to encourage students to compare their solutions with the one being shared.

Who else solved the problem in the same way? . . . Did anyone think about the problem differently?

Ursula, you saw this case of juice as an array of 8 × 9 when it was full. How did you figure out the product of 8 times 9? Was there another multiplication combination you knew that helped you?

I looked at the top cans and $5 \times 8 = 40$ so that's part of the total   I know the rest of the array is 4×8 which is 32. $40 + 32 = 72$

Sample Student Work

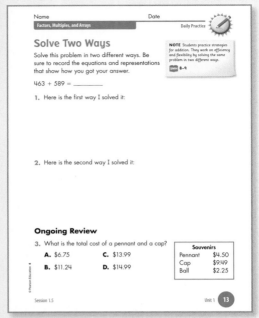

▲ **Student Activity Book, p. 13**

▲ **Student Activity Book, p. 14**

Benson, you said you used the packs of 3 juice cans to help you. Can you explain how you figured out how many 3-packs there were?

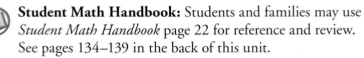

I saw 8 groups of 3 cans in the top section. And I know that 8 × 3 is 24. The middle is the same amount and the bottom is the same also. So the total is 24 + 24 + 24 = 72.

Sample Student Work

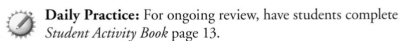

SESSION FOLLOW-UP
③ Daily Practice and Homework

Daily Practice: For ongoing review, have students complete *Student Activity Book* page 13.

Homework: On *Student Activity Book* page 14, students solve three related story problems involving time and multiplication.

Student Math Handbook: Students and families may use *Student Math Handbook* page 22 for reference and review. See pages 134–139 in the back of this unit.

Mathematical Emphases

Whole Number Operations Understanding and working with an array model of multiplication

Math Focus Points
◆ Using arrays to model multiplication situations

Whole Number Operations Reasoning about numbers and their factors

Math Focus Points
◆ Determining whether one number is a factor or multiple of another

Computational Fluency Fluency with multiplication combinations to 12×12

Math Focus Points
◆ Identifying and learning multiplication combinations not yet known fluently

◆ Using known multiplication combinations to determine the products of more difficult combinations

Multiplication Combinations

SESSION 2.1 p. 58	Student Activity Book	Student Math Handbook	Professional Development: Read Ahead of Time	
Quick Images Students are introduced to the Ten-Minute Math activity *Quick Images,* in which they visualize and describe multiplication situations. They discuss strategies for learning multiplication combinations.	15	29–34	• **Part 4: Ten-Minute Math** in *Implementing Investigations in Grade 4:* Quick Images • **Dialogue Box:** Strategies for Learning Hard Combinations, p. 131	
SESSION 2.2 p. 64				
Multiplication Cards Students create a set of Multiplication Cards to practice and become fluent with all multiplication combinations to 12×12.	16–18	29–34	• **Teacher Note:** Learning and Assessing Multiplication Combinations, p. 120	
SESSION 2.3 p. 68				
Multiple Turn Over Students review the terms *factor* and *multiple,* and play a game, *Multiple Turn Over,* that provides experience with factors and multiples.	19–22	22, 24, 25; G9	• **Part 5: Technology in** *Investigations* in *Implementing Investigations in Grade 4:* Using Calculators with the Curriculum • **Dialogue Box:** Identifying Factors and Multiples in *Multiple Turn Over,* p. 133	
SESSION 2.4 p. 76				
Multiplication Combinations Students discuss strategies for identifying factors and multiples in *Multiple Turn Over.* They work on three Math Workshop activities that focus on becoming fluent with multiplication combinations.	23–24	26; G6, G9		

Materials to Gather	Materials to Prepare
• **Students' lists of "Combinations I Know/Combinations I'm Working On"** (from Session 1.4)	• **T24–T25, *Quick Images: Seeing Numbers*** Cut apart images on transparencies, and pull out Images 1 and 2 for this session. • **Chart paper** Divide chart paper into two columns, and label them "Combinations We're Working On" and "Start With."
• **Array Cards** (1 deck per student from Session 1.4; optional) • **Scissors** (1 per student) • **Paper clips** (1 per student) • **Envelopes or resealable plastic bags** (1 per student)	• **M35–M40, Multiplication Cards** Make copies. (1 set per student) • **M41, Blank Multiplication Cards** Make copies and cut apart cards. (optional) • **M42, Practicing with Multiplication Cards** Make copies. (as needed) • **M43–M44, Family Letter** Make copies. (1 per student)
• **T26, *Multiple Turn Over* Recording Sheet** • **Calculators** (1 per student; optional)	• **M41, Blank Multiplication Cards** Make copies. (1 per student, for homework) • **M45, *Multiple Turn Over*** Make copies. (as needed) • **M46–M49, Multiple Cards** Make copies. (Copying these on different-color paper will make it easier for pairs to identify their deck.) Use a paper cutter to cut apart the cards. (1 set per pair) • **M50, *Multiple Turn Over* Recording Sheet** Make copies. (as needed) • **Chart paper** Label a sheet of chart paper "Factors and Multiples." • **Chart Paper** Divide chart paper into three columns (or draw on the board). Label them "Factor," "Multiple," and "Yes or No?"
• **M42, Practicing with Multiplication Cards** (as needed; from Session 2.2) • **Array Cards** (1 set per pair; from Session 1.4) • **Multiplication Cards** (1 set per student; from Session 2.2) • **Multiple Cards** (1 deck per pair; from Session 2.3) • **Calculators** (optional)	• **M41, Blank Multiplication Cards** Make copies. (1 per student, for homework) • **M42, Practicing with Multiplication Cards** • **M50, *Multiple Turn Over* Recording Sheet** Make copies. (1 per student)

Overhead Transparency

Multiplication Combinations, *continued*

SESSION 2.5 p. 80	Student Activity Book	Student Math Handbook	Professional Development: Read Ahead of Time	
Assessment: Multiplication Combinations Students continue work on three Math Workshop activities that focus on becoming fluent with multiplication combinations. They also complete an assessment activity that focuses on multiplication combinations through 12×12.	25–26	29–34; G6, G9		

Materials to Gather	Materials to Prepare
• **M9–M29, Array Cards** (1 set per pair; from Session 1.4) • **M35–M40, Multiplication Cards** (1 set per student; from Session 2.2) • **M42, Practicing with Multiplication Cards** (as needed; from Session 2.2) • **M46–M49, Multiple Cards** (1 deck per pair; from Session 2.3) • **M50, *Multiple Turn Over* Recording Sheet** (as needed; from Session 2.4) • **Calculators** (optional)	• **M51, Multiplication Combinations** Make copies. (1 per student) • **M52, Blank Multiplication Combinations** Make copies. (as needed; optional)

Quick Images

Math Focus Points

◆ Using arrays to model multiplication situations

◆ Identifying and learning multiplication combinations not yet known fluently

◆ Using known multiplication combinations to determine the products of more difficult combinations

Vocabulary

product

Today's Plan

		Materials
ACTIVITY **1 Introducing** *Quick Images*	20 MIN CLASS	• T24–T25*
ACTIVITY **2 Combinations We're Working On**	20 MIN GROUPS	• Students' lists of "Combinations I Know/Combinations I'm Working On" (from Session 1.4)
DISCUSSION **3 Multiplication Strategies**	20 MIN CLASS	• Groups' lists of difficult combinations; chart: "Combinations We're Working On"*
SESSION FOLLOW-UP **4 Daily Practice**		• *Student Activity Book,* p. 15 • *Student Math Handbook,* pp. 29–34

*See *Materials to Prepare,* p. 55.

Ten-Minute Math

Note: The Ten-Minute Math activity for this Investigation, *Quick Images: Seeing Numbers,* is introduced in this session. Plan to do today's Ten-Minute Math sometime after math class, if possible. If not, choose an activity, such as *Today's Number,* with which your students are familiar.

Quick Images: Seeing Numbers Show *Quick Images: Seeing Numbers* (T24), Image 1. Ask students to write several different equations to find the total number of dots. For the first two viewings, give students 3 seconds to look at the pattern; the third time, leave the image displayed. Have two or three students explain how they saw the image (including any revisions they made) and their equations, showing how their numbers match the pattern. For example, Image 1 is an arrangement showing 5 groups of 4. Students might say $5 \times 4 = 20$, or $8 + 8 + 4 = 20$.

ACTIVITY

① Introducing *Quick Images*

20 MIN   CLASS

Quick Images: Seeing Numbers is introduced in this session and will continue as a Ten-Minute Math activity throughout Investigation 2 and into the beginning of Investigation 3. The *Quick Images* in this unit show equal groups of dots arranged in various patterns. These arrangements are designed to give students practice visualizing and combining equal groups.❶

As in all *Quick Image* activities, students see the image briefly so that they do not have time to count or add. Rather, they are encouraged to think about the groups of dots they can see in the pattern. The students' task is to describe how they saw the arrangement of dots and how they determined the total number of dots in the image. Because there are different ways to describe the arrangement of each image, students also see how a number can be broken up into different combinations of factors. Begin by briefly displaying the transparency of Image 1 (T24).

After briefly viewing a Quick Image *pattern, students explain how they visualized and combined equal groups.*

Show students the image for three seconds before covering it or turning off the overhead projector. Some students may find it useful to draw the arrangement of dots in their mental image; others may jot down information about what they saw or write equations to help them make sense of the image.

After one or two minutes have passed, flash the image again for three seconds and allow students to revise their drawings, notes, or equations on the basis of this second viewing. When student activity subsides again,

---

Professional Development

❶ **Part 4: Ten-Minute Math** in *Implementing Investigations in Grade 4: Quick Images*

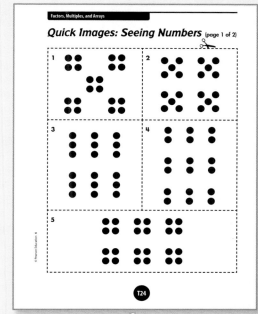

▲ **Transparencies, T24** 🖨 ;
Resource Masters, M33

show the image a third time. This time, leave it visible so that all students can complete or revise their drawings, notes, or equations.

When students have finished, raise the following questions:

How were you able to remember this image after seeing it briefly?

What did you notice in the image that helped you?

How many dots are there altogether in this image?

Students might say:

"I saw five groups of dots. There were 4 dots in each group. I know that 5 × 4 = 20, so there are 20 dots altogether."

"I saw two groups of 4 dots in the top row, two groups in the bottom row, and one group in the middle. The two groups in the top row equal 8 dots, and the two in the bottom are 8 more. That's 16, plus the 4 in the middle makes 20 dots."

Help students think of equations to represent their thinking. For example, the mental image described by the girl above can be represented as follows:

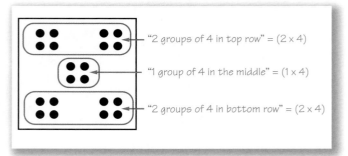

Now, or at another time outside of math class, display Image 2 and repeat the *Quick Image* steps described above.

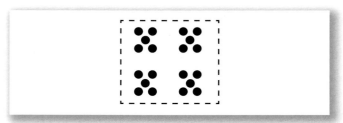

Students might say:

"I saw 4 groups of 5 dots. I know that 4 × 5 = 20, so there are 20 dots altogether."

"It's like the first one we did except instead of 5 groups of 4 dots, there are 4 groups of 5 dots. The total for both is 20."

ACTIVITY

20 MIN GROUPS

② Combinations We're Working On

Using their lists of "Combinations I Know" and "Combinations I'm Working On" from previous sessions, groups of four work together to make a list of the five multiplication combinations that they think are the most difficult to learn.

Groups consult their lists as they decide on the five most difficult multiplication combinations.

After you've made your list of the five most difficult combinations, I'd like you to work together, using multiplication combinations you know to help you learn and remember these difficult combinations. For example, if 8 × 7 is a hard combination for your group, but you do know 4 × 7, try using 4 × 7 to help you figure out 8 × 7.

Explain to the students that they will be coming back together as a whole class to share their five difficult combinations and to talk more about strategies for learning difficult combinations.

Professional Development

❷ **Dialogue Box:** Strategies for Learning Hard Combinations, p. 131

Differentiation

❸ **English Language Learners** Check that students know *start with* and other vocabulary related to this discussion. Choose a problem and describe and model a strategy that students might use to figure it out. "To figure out 6 × 4, I can *start with* 3 times 4. (Build a 3 × 4 array with the cubes.) I know this *combination* equals 12. Then for 6 times 4, I will *double* the answer. (Build another 3 × 4 array with cubes to demonstrate doubling and the resulting 6 × 4 array.)" To reinforce vocabulary, ask English Language Learners to explain the strategy in their own words.

ONGOING ASSESSMENT: Observing Students at Work

Students use knowledge of multiplication combinations they know to find ones they do not yet know.

- **Can students use combinations they know to help them identify combinations they do not yet know?** ("I know 9 × 9 because it is a square number, so 8 × 9 is one group of 9 less.")

- **Do students identify useful relationships among multiplication combinations?** ("I know that 6 × 9 is made up of three groups of 2 × 9.")

DISCUSSION

③ Multiplication Strategies

20 MIN CLASS

Math Focus Points for Discussion

◆ Using known multiplication combinations to determine the products of more difficult combinations

Ask each group to present the list of multiplication combinations that its members prepared in the previous activity.❷ On the chart paper you prepared, under the heading "Combinations We're Working On," list students' responses. There are likely to be multiplication combinations common to many groups' lists. Rather than recording these pairs more than once, put a check mark next to any that are repeated. When the list is complete, choose one of the multiplication combinations listed by several groups.

Most groups think that [6 × 8] is a hard combination to remember. If your group worked on this combination, what did you think of to help you get started finding the **product**?

Record students' responses on the chart paper under the "Start With" heading, alongside the multiplication combination you are discussing. Each time a student suggests a starting combination, ask what the next step would be and record this as well.❸

Combinations We're Working On	Start With
6 × 8	5 × 8 (and add one more 8)
	3 × 8 (and double it)
	6 × 4 (and double it)

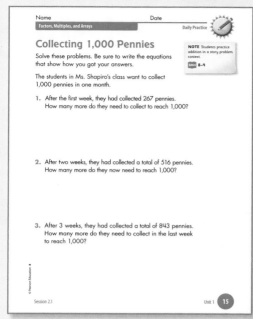

Name _____ **Date** _____

Factors, Multiples, and Arrays   Daily Practice

Collecting 1,000 Pennies

Solve these problems. Be sure to write the equations that show how you got your answers.

> **NOTE** Students practice addition in a story problem context.
> **Skill** 8–9

The students in Ms. Shapiro's class want to collect 1,000 pennies in one month.

1. After the first week, they had collected 267 pennies. How many more do they need to collect to reach 1,000?

2. After two weeks, they had collected a total of 516 pennies. How many more do they now need to reach 1,000?

3. After 3 weeks, they had collected a total of 843 pennies. How many more do they need to collect in the last week to reach 1,000?

Session 2.1   Unit 1   **15**

▲ **Student Activity Book, p. 15**

Emphasize that, although there are many starting places for solving each multiplication combination, students should think about ones they can use easily. This is because the idea is to find the solution quickly. Choose another multiplication combination. Ask students to share starting places for this combination. Then post the chart where students can return to it, both for reference and to record starting places for other combinations as they review and practice over the next few sessions.

During this discussion, use pictures, arrays, and story contexts from Investigation 1 (or others that students come up with) to help students visualize how one multiplication combination can help with another.

SESSION FOLLOW-UP
④ Daily Practice

 Daily Practice: For ongoing review, have students complete *Student Activity Book* page 15.

 Student Math Handbook: Students and families may use *Student Math Handbook* pages 29–34 for reference and review. See pages 134–139 in the back of this unit.

Multiplication Cards

Math Focus Points

◆ Identifying and learning multiplication combinations not yet known fluently

◆ Using known multiplication combinations to determine the products of more difficult combinations

Today's Plan		Materials
ACTIVITY **❶ Multiplication Cards**	60 MIN INDIVIDUALS PAIRS	• M9–M29 (optional); M35–M40*; M41, (optional)*; M42 (as needed)* • Scissors; paper clips; envelopes or resealable plastic bags
SESSION FOLLOW-UP **❷ Daily Practice and Homework**		• *Student Activity Book,* pp. 16–18 • *Student Math Handbook,* pp. 29–34 • M43–M44, Family Letter*

*See *Materials to Prepare,* p. 55.

Ten-Minute Math

Quick Images: Seeing Numbers Show *Quick Images: Seeing Numbers* (T24), Image 2. Ask students to write several different equations to find the total number of dots. For the first two viewings, give students 3 seconds to look at the pattern; the third time, leave the image displayed. Have two or three students explain how they saw the image (including any revisions they made) and their equations, showing how their numbers match the pattern. For example, Image 2 is an arrangement showing 4 groups of 5. Students might say $4 \times 5 = 20$ or $2 \times 10 = 20$.

ACTIVITY
Multiplication Cards

60 MIN INDIVIDUAL PAIRS

Tell students that the Multiplication Cards (M35–M40) include all the multiplication combinations up to 12×12 except for the combinations for 0, 1, and 2, which you expect that they know already from their work in Grade 3.❶

Have each student prepare a set of Multiplication Cards as follows:

- Cut the cards apart and write the product on the back of each card, along with the student's initials, so that each student's cards can be identified. Students may refer to their Array Cards (M9–M29) to help them with the more difficult combinations.❷

- Sort the cards into two sets: a "just know" pile, meaning that the student can find the product correctly and quickly without having to stop and figure it out, and a "working on" pile. Paper-clip the "just know" cards together, and put them away in an envelope or resealable plastic bag.

- Practice with the "working on" cards by looking at each multiplication combination and thinking of a combination the student already knows that can help him or her learn this one. Write that multiplication combination on the front of the card after the words *Start With*.

Name _____ Date _____

Factors, Multiples, and Arrays

Multiplication Cards (page 1 of 6)

3×3	3×4 4×3
Start with _____	Start with _____
3×5 5×3	3×6 6×3
Start with _____	Start with _____
3×7 7×3	3×8 8×3
Start with _____	Start with _____
3×9 9×3	3×11 11×3
Start with _____	Start with _____

Session 2.2   Unit 1 **M35**

▲ **Resource Masters, M35–M40**

Math Note

❶ **Multiplying by 0** Students are sometimes confused when they encounter multiplying by 0. It may be useful to start with other multiplication combinations that students know, put them in a context, then extend the context to multiplication by 0. For example, if I have 2 apples in each of 5 bags, I have 10 apples ($5 \times 2 = 10$); if I have 1 apple in each of 5 bags, I have 5 apples ($5 \times 1 = 5$); if I have 0 apples in each of the 5 bags, I have 0 apples ($5 \times 0 = 0$). Students can visualize or act out these situations.

Teaching Note

❷ **Using Arrays** Encourage students to have their Array Cards available as they make their Multiplication Cards. Some students begin to visualize the multiplication combinations as arrays, and this can help them find and remember the product of combinations they do not yet know fluently. For example, a student visualizing 8×9 may realize that it is one row of 9 less than 9×9; or a student might visualize 8×6 as two groups of 8×3.

Professional Development

❸ **Teacher Note:** Learning and Assessing Multiplication Combinations, p. 120

Name _____ Date _____

Factors, Multiples, and Arrays

Blank Multiplication Cards ✂

_____ × _____   _____ × _____
_____ × _____   _____ × _____
Start with _____   Start with _____

_____ × _____   _____ × _____
_____ × _____   _____ × _____
Start with _____   Start with _____

_____ × _____   _____ × _____
_____ × _____   _____ × _____
Start with _____   Start with _____

_____ × _____   _____ × _____
_____ × _____   _____ × _____
Start with _____   Start with _____

Session 2.2   Unit 1 **M41**

▲ Resource Masters, M41

Name _____ Date _____

Factors, Multiples, and Arrays

Practicing with Multiplication Cards

1. Look at the front of each Multiplication Card. If you have a helper, that person can show you one card at a time.

2. Look at the card, and say the answer to the problem as quickly as you can. If you say the correct answer right away, put that card in the pile of combinations that you "just know." If you have to stop and figure the answer out, put that card in a pile of combinations that you are still "working on."

3. Paper-clip your "just know" cards together, and set them aside.

4. Look at each card in your "working on" pile. Think of an easy multiplication combination, one that you already know, that can help you remember this one. Write the easy combination on the line that says "Start with _____."

   Example: "I know that 7 × 7 = 49, so 6 × 7 must be one 7 less—that's 42."

   | 6 × 7 |
   | 7 × 6 |
   | Start with 7 × 7 |

5. Go through each of the cards in your "working on" pile at least 3 times, using your "start with" combinations to help you find the answers.

6. Put all of your cards together again, both "just know" and "working on," and go through them again.

7. Over the next few weeks, keep practicing until you have no more cards in your "working on" pile. Practice at school when you have extra time and practice at home with a family member.

M42 Unit 1   Session 2.2

▲ Resource Masters, M42

Individually or with a partner, students should go through their "working on" cards at least three times. They then take out the rest of their cards and mix all of them together. To finish this practice routine, they go through the entire set of Multiplication Cards, trying to find the products both quickly and correctly for as many of them as they can. As before, when they need to stop and figure out a particular combination, they place that one aside to make a set of combinations that they are still working on. They write easy combinations as starting places on these cards if they have not already done so.❸

Encourage students to repeat this practice routine when they have a few minutes, either outside of math time or during math when they have completed another task. They may also work on these for homework. Make available copies of Practicing with Multiplication Cards (M42) as a reminder of the routine. Let students know that their goal is to have all of the multiplication combinations to 12 × 12 "at their fingertips" when they start to work on problems with larger numbers.

ONGOING ASSESSMENT: Observing Students at Work

Students use multiplication combinations they know to help them solve and commit to memory others with which they are not yet fluent.

- **Do students know most of the multiplication combinations with products to 50 (which was the focus in Grade 3)?** Are they fluent with 2s, 5s, and 10s?

- **Can students relate one multiplication combination to another in order to learn less familiar combinations (e.g., knowing that 3 × 11 is the same as adding one more 3 to 3 × 10)?**

DIFFERENTIATION: Supporting the Range of Learners

As you assess your students' knowledge of the multiplication combinations, focus each student's attention on groups of facts that he or she has not yet mastered.

(Intervention) The ×2 combinations are not included in the set of Multiplication Cards. Students who need to review the multiplication combinations with 2 as a factor may make an additional set of cards from the Blank Multiplication Cards (M41).

(ELL) If a student knows the combinations but is struggling with number names, partner this student with one who is fluent with the names but needs practice with the combinations.

SESSION FOLLOW-UP
2 Daily Practice and Homework

 Daily Practice: For ongoing review, have students complete *Student Activity Book* page 16.

 Homework: On *Student Activity Book* pages 17–18, students look at two pictured Array Cards, each one showing the factor side of the array. Their task is to determine what is on the other side— the product—of each Array Card and explain how they know.

 Student Math Handbook: Students and families may use *Student Math Handbook* pages 29–34 for reference and review. See pages 134–139 in the back of this unit.

 Family Letter: Send home copies of the Family Letter (M43–M44).

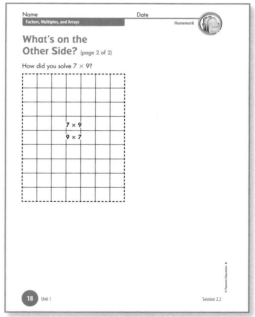

▲ Student Activity Book, p. 18

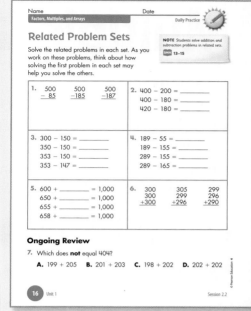

▲ Student Activity Book, p. 16

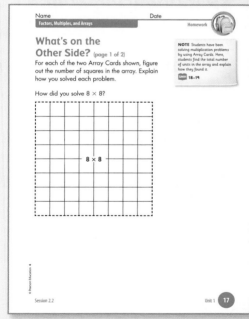

▲ Student Activity Book, p. 17

Multiple Turn Over

Math Focus Points

- Determining whether one number is a factor or multiple of another
- Identifying and learning multiplication combinations not yet known fluently
- Using known multiplication combinations to determine the products of more difficult combinations

Vocabulary

multiple
factor

Today's Plan		Materials
ACTIVITY **① Finding Factors and Multiples** 20 MIN · INDIVIDUALS · PAIRS		• Chart: "Factors and Multiples"* • Chart: "Factors and Multiples: Yes or No?"* • Calculators (optional)
ACTIVITY **② Introducing *Multiple Turn Over*** 15 MIN · CLASS		• M45*; M46–M49*; M50* • T26
ACTIVITY **③ Playing *Multiple Turn Over*** 25 MIN · GROUPS · PAIRS		• *Student Activity Book*, p. 19 • M46–M49; M50 • Calculators (optional)
SESSION FOLLOW-UP **④ Daily Practice and Homework**		• *Student Activity Book*, pp. 20–22 • *Student Math Handbook*, pp. 22, 24, 25; G9 • M41*

*See *Materials to Prepare*, p. 55.

Ten-Minute Math

Quick Images: Seeing Numbers Show *Quick Images: Seeing Numbers* (T24), Images 3 and 4 (one at a time). For each pattern, ask students to write several different equations to find the total number of dots. For the first two viewings, give students 3 seconds to look at the pattern; the third time, leave the image displayed. Have two or three students explain how they saw the images (including any revisions they made) and their equations, showing how their numbers match the patterns.

ACTIVITY

Finding Factors and Multiples

20 MIN INDIVIDUALS PAIRS

Before introducing the game *Multiple Turn Over,* use this activity to reinforce the meaning of the terms *factor* and *multiple* and the difference between them.

Start by showing students the "Factors and Multiples" chart you prepared. Throughout the activity, add words and drawings to record students' ideas about factors and multiples. Post this chart where students can refer back to it throughout the Investigation.

Sometimes the words *factor* and *multiple* can be confusing. Let's talk about those terms while we make a class chart to help us remember the difference between them.

Try to think back to third grade, when you skip counted on a 100 chart. In skip counting, which numbers are factors and which numbers are multiples?

Students may recall that a factor is the number you are skip counting by (2s, 6s, 10s, etc.), and the multiples of that number are the numbers you land on while skip counting (6, 12, 18, etc.). Add an example of skip counting to the chart.

Factors and Multiples

Factor	Multiple
the number you count by when you skip count	the numbers you land on
2	2, 4, 6, 8, 10

Where do you land if you skip count by 5 four times? Six times? How would you write these as multiplication equations?

When students come up with the equations, write them on the board.

$$4 \times 5 = 20$$

$$6 \times 5 = 30$$

How do these equations show that 20 and 30 are multiples of 5?

Algebra Note

❶ Using Landmark Combinations When deciding whether 3 is a factor of 51, some students may use $10 \times 3 = 30$ as a landmark combination and then reason as follows:

$10 \times 3 = 30$

$51 - 30 = 21$

$7 \times 3 = 21$

So, $17 \times 3 = 51$.

Teaching Note

❷ Using Calculators to Find Factors Students may use calculators to find factors of some large 2-digit or 3-digit numbers. If your class is not familiar with the way a calculator could be used for this, spend 10 minutes exploring this with them. Students may realize that they can try out different factors by skip counting on the calculator (e.g., $6 + 6 + 6 + 6 \ldots$) or that they can use division ("$72 \div 6 = 12$, so I know that 6 and 12 are factors of 72"). Read Part 5 of *Implementing Investigations in Grade 4, Technology in Investigations:* Using Calculators with the Curriculum.

Listen for the understanding that 20 and 30 are multiples of 5 because they are the product found by multiplying 5 by a whole number.

How can you use the word *factor* for some of the numbers in the equations?

Students should understand that 4 and 5 are factors of 20 because their product is 20. Similarly, 5 and 6 are factors of 30. Add a labeled equation to the "Factors and Multiples" chart.

4	×	5	=	20
factor		factor		multiple

Next, turn students' attention to the three-column chart you prepared, "Factors and Multiples: Yes or No?" Write 3 in the "Factor" column and 51 in the "Multiple" column.

Factor	Multiple	Yes or No?
3	51	

Here's a problem for you: Is 3 a factor of 51? Turn to someone sitting near you and work together for a few minutes to answer that question.

Bring the class back together, and ask students to offer ways to solve the problem. ❶

Discuss various strategies, which might include the following:

- Think of the problem as a missing factor problem, $3 \times ? = 51$. Some students might first narrow their choices and try only numbers greater than 10 (because $3 \times 10 = 30$) and less than 20 (because $3 \times 20 = 60$).

- Think of the problem as division, $51 \div 3 = ?$ If the answer is a whole number, then 3 is a factor of 51.

- Skip count by adding 3s until 51 is reached. Some students will repeatedly add 3. Others may use a calculator and enter $3 + 3$ and then press the equal key repeatedly. ❷

Some students might use a calculator to determine whether one number is a factor of another.

Give students several more problems to try. Solicit responses to the new problems, and ask students to explain their reasoning.

Students might say:

"6 is not a factor of 86. I added 6 a lot of times on the calculator and didn't land on 86."

"4 is not a factor of 58. I know because 4 × 15 = 60, and 58 is only 2 less."

"9 is a factor of 108. I just know that 9 × 12 is 108."

ONGOING ASSESSMENT: Observing Students at Work

Students determine whether a number is a multiple of a given factor.

- **Are students using the terms factor and multiply correctly?**

- **How do students determine if one number is a factor of another?**
  Do they skip count? Use a calculator? Use what they know?

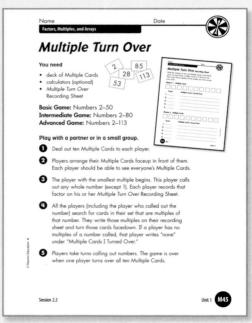

▲ Resource Masters, M46–M49

▲ Resource Masters, M45

As students work, notice the strategies they use. For example, if you see students skip counting on a calculator and starting at 0, suggest that they start with a multiplication combination that will get them as close as possible to the target number. Ask questions such as the following:

- I see that you're skip counting to see whether 9 is a factor of 108. You started at 0. Do you know a multiplication combination with 9 that will get you closer to 108? Do you know 10×9?

- You said that 10×9 is 90. That's like skip counting by 9 ten times. So start at 90, and see whether you can skip count to get to 108. How many more times did you have to skip count?

② ACTIVITY
Introducing *Multiple Turn Over*

15 MIN   CLASS

Multiple Turn Over is a game in which students are encouraged to use numerical reasoning based on what they know about factors and multiples, such as the facts that all even numbers are multiples of 2 and multiples of 5 must end in either 5 or 0.

Play a few rounds with the whole class, introducing the rules as explained on *Multiple Turn Over* (M45). For this introduction, limit the Multiple Cards to those in the intermediate set, 2–80. Randomly choose ten cards from that set, and draw them on the board (or display transparent cards). Instruct students to randomly choose ten cards from their own decks and place these cards face up in front of them.

Begin by naming a factor. Start with a small number such as 3. (Do not start with 2 because too many numbers are its multiples.) Players pick out all the multiples of 3 from among the numbers in front of them. They turn these cards facedown.

Circle the multiples of 3 among the Multiple Cards you have drawn on the board. Explain the thinking that has led you to select those cards.

The factor that I named was 3. I saw that I had the Multiple Card 15, and I selected it because $5 \times 3 = 15$. I also had the Multiple Card 48. I wasn't sure about this number, but I knew that $10 \times 3 = 30$. Because $6 \times 3 = 18$, I knew that six more 3s would get me from 30 to 48.

As you play, demonstrate how to keep track of each round on the transparent *Multiple Turn Over* Recording Sheet (T26). After you have recorded 15 and 48, erase the numbers on the cards you have drawn on the board to indicate that they are "turned over."

A volunteer then suggests another factor. All players pick out all the multiples of that number from among their remaining Multiple Cards and turn them over. Continue to model your own thinking as you select Multiple Cards from those left on the board, and ask for a couple of volunteers to model their thinking as well.

ACTIVITY

25 MIN | PAIRS | GROUPS

3 Playing *Multiple Turn Over*

Students play *Multiple Turn Over* in pairs or small groups for the remainder of the session. They use the recording sheet on *Student Activity Book* page 19. Have calculators available for use as desired, and make available extra recording sheets (M50) as needed. Let students know that they will also have time to play the game in the Math Workshops in the next two sessions. ❸ ❹

Multiple Turn Over *gives students practice with identifying multiples of a given number.*

▲ **Student Activity Book, p. 19; Resource Masters, M50; T26**

Name _____ Date _____
Factors, Multiples, and Arrays

Multiple Turn Over Recording Sheet
Write the numbers of your 10 Multiple Cards on the blank cards. As each factor is called, record it in the factor list. Then write which multiples of that number you have among your cards.

Game 1 Multiple Cards
□ □ □ □ □ □ □ □ □ □

Factor   Multiple Cards I Can Turn Over
1. _____   _____
2. _____   _____
3. _____   _____
4. _____   _____
5. _____   _____

Game 2 Multiple Cards
□ □ □ □ □ □ □ □ □ □

Factor   Multiple Cards I Can Turn Over
1. _____   _____
2. _____   _____
3. _____   _____
4. _____   _____
5. _____   _____

Session 2.3   Unit 1   19

Teaching Note

❸ **Winning Strategies** As students become accomplished at the game *Multiple Turn Over,* they develop strategies to help them become the first player to turn over all ten Multiple Cards. They become increasingly fluent with the multiples of each number. They learn to call factors of their own numbers that are *not* factors of the other player's numbers. They notice that they must name the number itself in order to turn over a prime number.

Professional Development

❹ **Dialogue Box:** Identifying Factors and Multiples in *Multiple Turn Over*, p. 133

Professional Development

⑤ **Part 5: Technology in *Investigations* in *Implementing Investigations in Grade 4:* Using Calculators with the Curriculum**

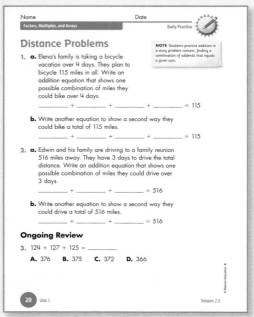

▲ **Student Activty Book, p. 20**

ONGOING ASSESSMENT: Observing Students at Work

Students solve problems in which they determine which numbers are multiples of a given number.

- **What characteristics of multiples do students use?** For example, do students know that even numbers are multiples of 2, or that multiples of 5 end in 5 or 0?

- **Do students use knowledge of multiplication combinations?** Do they recognize most products of multiplication combinations up to 12×12?

- **How do students determine factors of more difficult multiples?** Do they skip count? Do they reason from multiplication combinations they know?

- **Are students also considering the Multiple Cards in the other player's hand when they choose which factors to name?**

DIFFERENTIATION: Supporting the Range of Learners

There are three levels of *Multiple Turn Over*. Use your observations of the work students did with Multiplication Cards in Session 2.2, page 65, to help them determine the level at which they should begin.

Basic level (numbers 2–50) Those students still learning the multiplication facts with products to 50 should play the basic level, which students played in Grade 3.

Intermediate level (numbers 2–80) Most students will probably start with the intermediate level. This allows them to review the multiples to 50 they worked on in Grade 3, while using this knowledge to determine the factors of larger numbers.

Advanced level (numbers 2–113) Some students may be ready to work with all of the numbers in the deck and should start with the advanced level.

Intervention Some students will use the calculator to skip count to determine whether a number is a multiple of a particular factor. If you notice students skip counting from 0, ask questions to encourage them to start with a multiplication combination that will get them as close as possible to the target number.⑤ For example:

- I see that you're skip counting on the calculator to see whether 6 is a factor of 72. You started at 0, with 6 + 6. Is there a multiplication combination you know, with 6 as one of the factors, that will get you closer to 72? Do you know 6 × 6, or 10 × 6? Can you start with the product of one of those combinations?

- You said that 6 × 6 is 36, and that's like skip counting by 6 six times. If you start at 36, how many more times will you have to count by 6 to get to 72?

SESSION FOLLOW-UP
Daily Practice and Homework

 Daily Practice: For ongoing review, have students complete *Student Activity Book* page 20.

 Homework: For practice at home with the multiplication combinations to 12 × 12, have students fill in a copy of Blank Multiplication Cards (M41) with combinations from their "working on" sets. Suggest that they cut apart these cards at home and practice them with a friend or family member. *Student Activity Book* page 21 provides a reminder of the routine, and on page 22, students record how they worked on the combinations they have chosen.

 Student Math Handbook: Students and families may use *Student Math Handbook* pages 22, 24, 25 and G9 for reference and review. See pages 134–139 in the back of this unit.

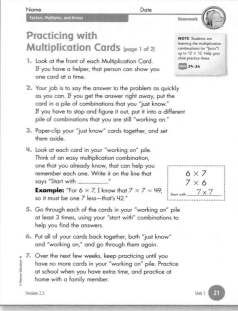

▲ **Student Activity Book, p. 21**

▲ **Student Activity Book, p. 22**

Multiplication Combinations

Math Focus Points

♦ Determining whether one number is a factor or multiple of another

♦ Identifying and learning multiplication combinations not yet known fluently

♦ Using known multiplication combinations to determine the products of more difficult combinations

Today's Plan		Materials
① DISCUSSION **Strategies for *Multiple Turn Over***	🕐 20 MIN 👥 CLASS	• M46–M49, Multiple Cards (from Session 2.3) (optional)
② MATH WORKSHOP **Multiplication Combinations** **②A** *Multiplication Cards* **②B** *Factor Pairs* **②C** *Multiple Turn Over*	🕐 40 MIN	**②A** • M35–M40, Multiplication Cards (from Session 2.2); M42 **②B** • M9–M29, Array Cards (from Session 1.4) • Blank paper **②C** • M46–M49; M50* • Calculators (optional)
③ SESSION FOLLOW-UP **Daily Practice and Homework**		• *Student Activity Book,* pp. 23–24 • *Student Math Handbook,* pp. 26; G6, G9 • M41*

*See *Materials to Prepare,* p. 55.

Ten-Minute Math

Quick Images: Seeing Numbers Show *Quick Images: Seeing Numbers* (T24–T25), Images 5 and 6 (one at a time). For each pattern, ask students to write several different equations to find the total number of dots. For the first two viewings, give students 3 seconds to look at the pattern; the third time, leave the image displayed. Have two or three students explain how they saw the images (including any revisions they made) and their equations, showing how their numbers match the patterns.

DISCUSSION
Strategies for *Multiple Turn Over*

20 MIN   CLASS

Math Focus Points for Discussion

◆ Determining whether one number is a factor or multiple of another

Begin the discussion by sharing an example of an imaginary game of *Multiple Turn Over* played by two students.

Let's suppose that Derek and Yuson are playing *Multiple Turn Over*. They have turned over some of their cards already. It's Derek's turn, and he needs our help deciding what his next move should be. These are the cards that the students still have face up in front of them.

Write the multiples shown below on chart paper or on the board.

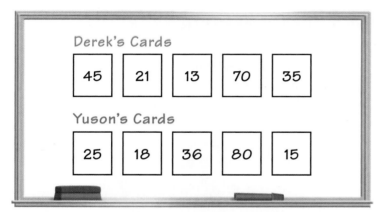

Derek's Cards

| 45 | 21 | 13 | 70 | 35 |

Yuson's Cards

| 25 | 18 | 36 | 80 | 15 |

What would be a good factor for Derek to name?

Ask students to talk to a partner about what factors Derek could name and which one they think would be his best move.

After a few minutes, elicit suggestions from the students, being sure to ask them to explain their reasons for naming a particular factor.

Students might say:

"Derek should name 3 because 3 is a factor of 45 and 21."

"I think he should name 5 because 5 is a factor of 45, 70, and 35."

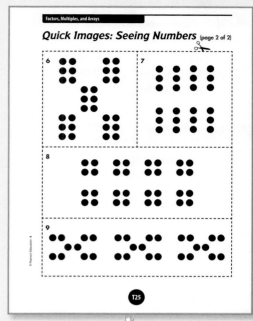

Factors, Multiples, and Arrays

Quick Images: Seeing Numbers (page 2 of 2)

T25

▲ Transparencies, T25 🖨;
Resource Masters, M34

Teaching Note

① **Working with Students** Use Math Workshop time to work with individuals or small groups. Continue to help students group multiplication combinations they have not yet mastered.

Professional Development

② **Teacher Note:** Learning and Assessing Multiplication Combinations, p. 120

Include questions such as the following in this discussion:

- If Derek names 5 [or another number] as a factor, what cards will he be able to turn over? What cards will Yuson turn over?

- When Yuson has her turn, what factor can she name that will allow her to turn over some of her cards without letting Derek turn over any of his?

- What factors can Yuson name if she wants to turn over the 36 in her hand? Will any of these factors allow her to turn over other cards?

If there is time, play out the two hands in a few different ways, following students' suggestions.

MATH WORKSHOP
2 Multiplication Combinations

40 MIN

Students work in pairs, either practicing multiplication combinations or working on factors and multiples. Use your observations of students' knowledge to suggest the most appropriate activities for each student.**①** Students will continue these Math Workshop activities in Session 2.5.

During Math Workshop, the teacher can help individuals or groups with multiplication combinations, factors, and multiples.

2A Multiplication Cards

PAIRS

For complete details about this activity, see Session 2.2, pages 65–66. Remind students to group the combinations they have not yet mastered in ways that might make them easier to learn.**②** Note that students are expected to know these combinations fluently by the end of Grade 4 and will continue to practice them throughout the year.

2B Factor Pairs

PAIRS

For complete details about this activity, see Session 1.4, pages 44–46.

2C Multiple Turn Over

PAIRS

For complete details about this activity, see Session 2.3, pages 72–75. Make sure that students are playing with Multiple Cards at an appropriate level of difficulty.

As an additional challenge for students playing at the advanced level (with all the Multiple Cards), ask that they play without using the factors 2 or 3.

SESSION FOLLOW-UP

③ Daily Practice and Homework

 Daily Practice: For ongoing review, have students complete *Student Activity Book* page 23.

 Homework: For continued practice with multiplication combinations, students take home another copy of Blank Multiplication Cards (M41) on which they have written combinations from their "working on" sets. On *Student Activity Book* page 24, they record how they worked on the combinations they have chosen.

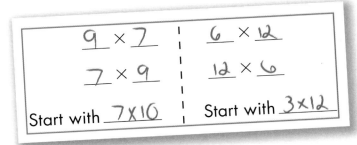

Sample Student Work

 Student Math Handbook: Students and families may use *Student Math Handbook* pages 26, G6 and G9 for reference and review. See pages 134–139 in the back of this unit.

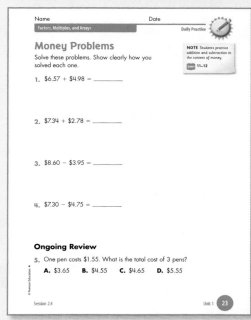

▲ **Student Activity Book, p. 23**

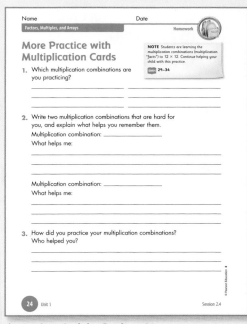

▲ **Student Activity Book, p. 24**

Assessment: Multiplication Combinations

Math Focus Points

◆ Identifying and learning multiplication combinations not yet known fluently

◆ Using known multiplication combinations to determine the products of more difficult combinations

◆ Determining whether one number is a factor or multiple of another

Today's Plan		Materials
MATH WORKSHOP ❶ **Multiplication Combinations,** *continued* ❶Ⓐ Multiplication Cards ❶Ⓑ *Factor Pairs* ❶Ⓒ *Multiple Turn Over*	50 MIN	Ⓐ • M35–M40, Multiplication Cards (from Session 2.2); M42 Ⓑ • M9–M29, Array Cards (from Session 1.4) Ⓒ • M46–M49, Multiple Cards (from Session 2.3); M50* • Calculators (optional)
ASSESSMENT ACTIVITY ❷ **Multiplication Combinations**	✓ 10 MIN INDIVIDUALS	• M51*; M52*
SESSION FOLLOW-UP ❸ **Daily Practice and Homework**		• *Student Activity Book,* pp. 25–26 • *Student Math Handbook,* pp. 29–34; G6, G9

*See *Materials to Prepare,* p. 57.

Ten-Minute Math

Quick Images: Seeing Numbers Show *Quick Images: Seeing Numbers* (T25), Images 7 and 8 (one at a time). For each pattern, ask students to write several different equations to find the total number of dots. For the first two viewings, give students 3 seconds to look at the pattern; the third time, leave the image displayed. Have two or three students explain how they saw the images (including any revisions they made) and their equations, showing how their numbers match the patterns.

MATH WORKSHOP

1 Multiplication Combinations, *continued*

50 MIN

Students continue working in pairs, either practicing multiplication combinations to 12 × 12 or playing games that involve the relationships between factors and multiples. By the end of this session, each student should have spent some time with *Multiple Turn Over* and at least one other Math Workshop activity.

Playing Factor Pairs *helps students practice multiplication combinations and identify those they still need to work on.*

1A Multiplication Cards

PAIRS

For complete details about this activity, see Session 2.2, pages 65–66. Remind students to group combinations they have not yet mastered.

1B *Factor Pairs*

PAIRS

For complete details about this activity, see Session 1.4, pages 44–46.

1C *Multiple Turn Over*

PAIRS

For complete details about this activity, see Session 2.3, pages 72–75.

Name _____ Date _____

Factors, Multiples, and Arrays

Assessment: Multiplication Combinations

8 × 5 =	4 × 7 =	3 × 9 =
7 × 9 =	3 × 12 =	6 × 4 =
3 × 6 =	9 × 4 =	7 × 6 =
12 × 4 =	5 × 7 =	8 × 8 =
9 × 9 =	6 × 6 =	5 × 6 =
11 × 6 =	8 × 9 =	6 × 12 =
3 × 8 =	5 × 12 =	8 × 6 =
5 × 9 =	3 × 7 =	7 × 8 =
7 × 10 =	8 × 4 =	7 × 7 =
9 × 6 =	12 × 12 =	8 × 12 =

Session 2.5   Unit 1 **M51**

▲ **Resource Masters, M51** *PORTFOLIO*

Resource Masters, M52

Blank Multiplication Combinations

Name _____ Date _____

Factors, Multiples, and Arrays

___ × ___ = ___	___ × ___ = ___
___ × ___ = ___	___ × ___ = ___
___ × ___ = ___	___ × ___ = ___
___ × ___ = ___	___ × ___ = ___
___ × ___ = ___	___ × ___ = ___
___ × ___ = ___	___ × ___ = ___
___ × ___ = ___	___ × ___ = ___
___ × ___ = ___	___ × ___ = ___
___ × ___ = ___	___ × ___ = ___
___ × ___ = ___	___ × ___ = ___

M52 Unit 1   Session 2.5

Teaching Note

① Explaining the Assessment Because timed work can make some students anxious, talk with them directly about why you want them to solve as many problems as they can in five minutes and how that will help both you and them find out which combinations they still need to work on. If students do seem anxious before the assessment, take time to discuss what could help them identify those problems they can tackle easily. Reassure students that they will continue to practice these combinations through the year. The assessment focuses on Benchmark 1: Use known multiplication combinations to find the product of any multiplication combination up to 12 × 12. Students will be assessed again on the multiplication combinations in the unit *Multiple Towers and Division Stories*.

Professional Development

② Teacher Note: Learning and Assessing Multiplication Combinations, p. 120

ASSESSMENT ACTIVITY

② Multiplication Combinations

10 MIN INDIVIDUALS

Multiplication Combinations (M51) has 30 combinations that range from 3 × 6 to 12 × 12, although not every combination within this range is included. For example, there is only one that involves multiplying by 10 (7 × 10) and only one that involves multiplying by 11 (11 × 6), because students generally recognize these patterns. There are also a few combinations that include 12 as one of the factors. Although these are traditionally considered multiplication facts to be learned, expect many students to break 12 into 10 and 2 and multiply the other factor by each of these. You might tell students to have scrap paper at hand for such work.

Most students should be able to solve these 30 multiplication problems in five minutes or less.

Students need to know that they should do the problems as quickly as they can. Explain that you are trying to help them learn which combinations they know readily and which they still need to work on.**①**

You will want to structure this assessment so that you get the information you want, without leaving students frustrated that they are not allowed to finish. One approach is to have students complete as many problems as they can in five minutes, skipping around to answer the ones they "just know" first. At the end of five minutes, they stop and circle the problems they have not yet solved. Then they continue solving these problems. This provides a record of which problems they needed more time to complete.**②**

ONGOING ASSESSMENT: Observing Students at Work

Students demonstrate fluency with multiplication combinations.

- **Are students able to accurately solve multiplication combinations that are presented in random order?**

- **Do students recognize the patterns for multiplying by 10 and 11?**
  Can they quickly solve problems that involve multiplying by 12?

DIFFERENTIATION: Supporting the Range of Learners

Intervention Although many students will know the majority of these combinations at this point, some students may need an opportunity either to take this assessment more than once or to continue practicing a few combinations that can be assessed individually later on. The assessment sheet may also be cut apart so that students are given fewer problems to solve at one time. When you know which combinations students still need to work on, you can use Blank Multiplication Combinations (M52) to create tailored assessments for ongoing use.

SESSION FOLLOW-UP
③ Daily Practice and Homework

 Daily Practice: For ongoing review, have students complete *Student Activity Book* page 25.

 Homework: On *Student Activity Book* page 26, students complete a chart of missing factors and products. Students are expected to use knowledge of the multiplication combinations they have been learning.

 Student Math Handbook: Students and families may use *Student Math Handbook* pages 29–34, G6 and G9 for reference and review. See pages 134–139 in the back of this unit.

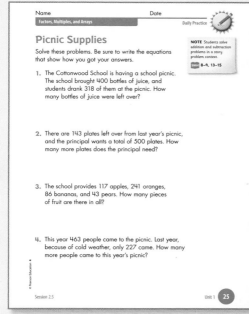

Name _____ Date _____

Factors, Multiples, and Arrays   Daily Practice

Picnic Supplies

Solve these problems. Be sure to write the equations that show how you got your answers.

NOTE Students solve addition and subtraction problems in a story problem context.
Skill 8–9, 13–15

1. The Cottonwood School is having a school picnic. The school brought 400 bottles of juice, and students drank 318 of them at the picnic. How many bottles of juice were left over?

2. There are 143 plates left over from last year's picnic, and the principal wants a total of 500 plates. How many more plates does the principal need?

3. The school provides 117 apples, 241 oranges, 86 bananas, and 43 pears. How many pieces of fruit are there in all?

4. This year 463 people came to the picnic. Last year, because of cold weather, only 227 came. How many more people came to this year's picnic?

Session 2.5   Unit 1 25

▲ **Student Activity Book, p. 25**

Name _____ Date _____

Factors, Multiples, and Arrays   Homework

Factors and Products

Fill in the chart with the missing factors or products.

NOTE Students are working to become fluent with multiplication combinations (also called multiplication "facts"). Here, they practice multiplication combinations by finding products or missing factors.
Skill 26, 29–34

Factor	×	Factor	=	Product
	×	8	=	16
4	×	7	=	
6	×		=	24
	×	5	=	30
3	×	9	=	
7	×		=	49
8	×	6	=	
10	×		=	100
	×	4	=	36

26 Unit 1   Session 2.5

▲ **Student Activity Book, p. 26**

Mathematical Emphases

Whole Number Operations Understanding and working with an array model of multiplication

Math Focus Points

◆ Using arrays to model multiplication situations

◆ Using arrays to find factors of 2-digit numbers

Whole Number Operations Reasoning about numbers and their factors

Math Focus Points

◆ Finding the multiples of a number by skip counting

◆ Identifying the factors of a given number

◆ Identifying all the factors of 100

◆ Using knowledge of the factors of 100 to find factors of multiples of 100

◆ Using known multiplication combinations to find related multiplication combinations for a given product (e.g., if $4 \times 50 = 200$, then $8 \times 25 = 200$)

◆ Using representations to show that a factor of a number is also a factor of its multiples (e.g., if 25 is a factor of 100, then 25 is also a factor of 300)

Computational Fluency Fluency with multiplication combinations to 12×12

Math Focus Points

◆ Using known multiplication combinations to determine the products of more difficult combinations

Finding Factors

	Student Activity Book	Student Math Handbook	Professional Development: Read Ahead of Time	
SESSION 3.1 p. 88				
Factors of 100 Students are introduced to a Ten-Minute Math activity, *Counting Around the Class,* in which they generate the multiples of a given number. They consider how the factors of 100 can help them find the factors of a multiple of 100 (200, 300, 400 . . .).	27–31	24–25	• **Part 4: Ten-Minute Math** in *Implementing Investigations in Grade 4:* Counting Around the Class	
SESSION 3.2 p. 96				
Factors of the Multiples of 100 Students find the factors of 200, 300, and other multiples of 100 by reasoning about the factors of 100 and other multiplication combinations they know.	28–29, 33–38	37–38		
SESSION 3.3 p. 105				
Factors of Related Numbers Students identify and represent the factors of 16 and 48 to explore the concept that the factors of a number are also factors of a multiple of that number.	39–42	26		
SESSION 3.4 p. 112				
End-of-Unit Assessment Students are assessed on the benchmarks of this unit. They solve and represent the product of a multiplication combination, and find and represent all the factors of 36.	43	23	• **Teacher Note:** End-of-Unit Assessment, p. 123	

Materials to Gather	Materials to Prepare
• **T27, 300 Chart** • **Connecting cubes or color tiles** (as needed) • **Calculators** (optional)	• **M2, Centimeter Grid Paper** Make copies. (as needed for use throughout Investigation 3) • **M53, Four 100 Charts** Make copies. (as needed for use throughout Investigation 3) • **M54, 300 Chart** Make copies. (as needed for use throughout Investigation 3) • **Chart paper** Write the title "Factor Pairs of 100" on chart paper.
• **M2, Centimeter Grid Paper** (as needed; from Session 3.1) • **M53, Four 100 Charts** (as needed; from Session 3.1) • **M54, 300 Chart** (as needed; from Session 3.1) • **Connecting cubes or color tiles** (as needed)	• **Chart paper** Write the title "Ideas About Factors of Multiples of 100" on chart paper.
• **M2, Centimeter Grid Paper** (as needed; from Session 3.1) • **Connecting cubes or color tiles** (as needed) • **Calculators** (optional)	
• **M2, Centimeter Grid Paper** (as needed; from Session 3.1)	• **M55–M56, End-of-Unit Assessment** Make copies. (1 per student)

Overhead Transparency

Factors of 100

Math Focus Points

- Identifying all the factors of 100
- Using knowledge of the factors of 100 to find factors of multiples of 100
- Finding the multiples of a number by skip counting

Today's Plan		Materials
1 ACTIVITY *Counting Around the Class*	15 MIN CLASS	
2 ACTIVITY *Finding the Factors of 100*	10 MIN INDIVIDUALS PAIRS	• *Student Activity Book,* p. 27 • M2*; M53* • Connecting cubes or color tiles • Calculators (optional)
3 DISCUSSION *Identifying All the Factors*	20 MIN CLASS	• *Student Activity Book,* p. 27 (students' completed work) • Chart: "Factor Pairs of 100"
4 ACTIVITY *Factors of 200 and 300*	15 MIN CLASS	• *Student Activity Book,* pp. 28–29 • M54* (as needed) • T27 • Calculators (optional)
5 SESSION FOLLOW-UP *Daily Practice and Homework*		• *Student Activity Book,* pp. 30–31 • *Student Math Handbook,* pp. 24–25

*See *Materials to Prepare,* p. 87.

Ten-Minute Math

Quick Images: Seeing Numbers **Show** *Quick Images: Seeing Numbers* **(T25), Image 9. Ask students to write several different equations to find the total number of dots. For the first two viewings, give students 3 seconds to look at the pattern; the third time, leave the image displayed. Have two or three students explain how they saw the image (including any revisions they made) and their equations, showing how their numbers match the pattern.**

ACTIVITY
Counting Around the Class

15 MIN   CLASS

Professional Development

❶ Part 4: Ten-Minute Math in *Implementing Investigations in Grade 4: Counting Around the Class*

Students may remember the Ten-Minute Math activity *Counting Around the Class* from their work in Grade 3. Briefly remind students that you will be counting by a certain number, with each student saying the next multiple in the sequence.

If we were counting around the class by 2s, Luke would say "2," Jill would say "4," and Enrique would say "6." But we're going to count by a more challenging number.

Tell students that they will be counting around the class by 6s. Before beginning the count, ask students to make an estimate.

If we count around the class by 6s and everyone says one number, what number will we end up on?

Collect a few responses, asking students to briefly explain the reasoning behind their answers.

Students might say:

"I know that we have about 20 students in our class. 10 × 6 = 60, and twice that would be 120."

Begin the count, recording each multiple of 6 on the board as it is called out. Stop after a student has said 36.

The last multiple of 6 someone said was 36. How many students have counted off so far? What multiplication combinations do you know that can help you figure this out?

Students might say:

"I know that 5 × 6 = 30. One more 6 would be 36, so 6 people have counted so far."

"I know that 2 × 6 = 12, and three 12s equal 36, so 6 people have counted so far."

Teaching Note

❷ Factors of 100 Most fourth graders should be familiar with the factors of 100. This short activity is meant as an introduction to the rest of the work in this Investigation.

Name _____ **Date** _____

Factors, Multiples, and Arrays

Finding the Factors of 100

Find the factors of 100. You may use the 100 chart, cubes, arrays, grid paper, or drawings to help you make sure that the numbers you choose are factors. Record the factors in the chart.

Factor	How Many in 100?	Factor Pair
Example: 1	100	100 × 1

When you think you have found all of the factors of 100, list them here.

_____

_____

Session 3.1   Unit 1 **27**

▲ **Student Activity Book, p. 27**

Name _____ **Date** _____

Factors, Multiples, and Arrays

Four 100 Charts

Session 3.1   Unit 1 **M53**

▲ **Resource Masters, M53**

"I know my square numbers, and 6 × 6 = 36, so 6 people have counted."

Continue the count and stop at the multiple 72, once again raising the question of how many people have counted so far. As the students respond, listen for what understandings of number relationships their responses indicate.

- Do they use the information that 72 is double 36 to help them solve the problem?

- Do they use 10 × 6 = 60 as a landmark and realize that 2 more counts of 6 will get them to 72?

Finish by completing the count and comparing their final number to their initial estimate.

ACTIVITY

❷ Finding the Factors of 100

10 MIN INDIVIDUALS PAIRS

Explain to students that for the next ten minutes they will work alone or with a partner to find all the factors of 100 and record their findings on *Student Activity Book* page 27.❷

Encourage students to use the multiplication combinations they know to help them find other combinations. For this work, students can also refer to the Four 100 Charts (M53); draw or build arrays using Centimeter Grid Paper (M2), connecting cubes, or color tiles; or use calculators.

As you're working on this problem, think about what factors you already know you can multiply to get a product of 100. What numbers do you know that can't possibly be factors of 100? When are you pretty sure that you have all the factors? We'll come back and talk about these questions. You'll have about 10 minutes to find as many of the factors of 100 as you can.

As students work, encourage those who have not found all the factors yet to keep looking.

Some students divide grids of 100 into equal sections to identify numbers that are and are not factors of 100.

ONGOING ASSESSMENT: Observing Students at Work

Students use knowledge of multiplication combinations they know and reasoning about number relationships to generate all the factors of 100.

- **Are students trying numbers randomly, or are they choosing numbers on the basis of known relationships between those numbers and 100?** ("I know that I can skip count to 100 by 5s because we counted five 20s to get to 100.")

- **Are students using what they know about one factor of 100 to make conjectures about a related factor?** ("I know that I can make an array of 100 with 10s, so I must be able to make an array with 5s too, because I could cut all the rows of 10 into rows of 5.")

- **Do students use reason about number relationships to determine that some numbers cannot be factors of 100?** ("Any number larger than 50 can't be a factor because $2 \times 50 = 100$, and 2 times anything bigger would be more than 100.")

DIFFERENTIATION: Supporting the Range of Learners

Intervention Students who are having some trouble identifying the factors may find it useful to think about money.

- How can you split up a dollar evenly?

- What multiplication equations can you write to show how you would split up one dollar? ("Four quarters equal a dollar, so $4 \times 25 = 100$.")

Extension Students who quickly generate all the factors can write a response to the question, "How do you know that you have all the factors?" in preparation for the following discussion.

DISCUSSION
3 Identifying All the Factors

20 MIN   CLASS

Math Focus Points for Discussion

◆ Identifying all the factors of 100

Call on students to name factors of 100 they identified, and make a list of all the factors the class found. (They may not have found them all.) Ask students to share the methods they used to find the factors. These might include skip counting, dividing 100 into equal groups, making arrays, reasoning from known combinations, or thinking about money. Use the following questions as guidelines for a discussion about the numbers on the class list.

• How do you know that 20 is a factor?

• How does [Lucy's] array of [5 × 20] show the same thing as skip counting by 20? Where are the groups of 20 in the array? Where are they on [Noemi's] 100 chart?

• What numbers did you try that didn't work? How do you know that [32] doesn't work?

• Were there any numbers that you were sure you did not have to try? How did you know?

• Did anyone try 49? Could it work? Why or why not?

As students respond, try to move the conversation from a focus on *individual* numbers that have been tried (*"I know that 26 doesn't work because I tried it."*) to more *general notions* about how to eliminate numbers that are not factors. (*"You don't have to test anything above 50 because you can't multiply 51, or any higher number, by any whole number and get a number less than 100."*)

Do we have all of the factors of 100 on our list? Is there a way that we could organize the list to make it easier to see whether we have them all?

Take students' suggestions, which should include making sure that they have both factors in each pair of factors listed. Write the pairs of factors for 100 in order on the chart paper.❸

Factor Pairs for 100

1 × 100 (or 100 × 1)

2 × 50 (or 50 × 2)

4 × 25 (or 25 × 4)

5 × 20 (or 20 × 5)

10 × 10

Teaching Note

❸ **Classroom Display**   Keep this "Factor Pairs for 100" chart posted for future reference. You may also want to include visual references with the list, such as highlighted 100 charts and any arrays or connecting cube models that students constructed.

ACTIVITY

4 Factors of 200 and 300

15 MIN   CLASS

What are some factors of 200? . . . How do you know that you've found a factor of 200?

Take just one or two examples, and then tell students that next they will be finding the factors of 200 and 300. If any students have already brought up the idea that a factor of 100 is also a factor of 200, explore this concept.

[Jake] said that 20 is a factor of 200 because it's a factor of 100. Are other factors of 100 also factors of 200? Are they factors of 300? I'd like you to keep thinking about this question as you work, and we'll talk about it in the next session.

If students have not yet brought up this concept, you can wait until tomorrow's discussion, when students will have more experience working with the factors of 200 and 300.

Again, remind students about the math tools that are available.

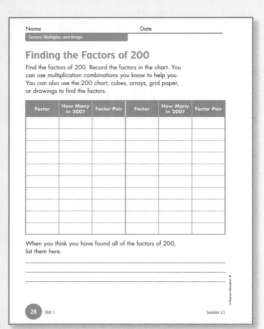

Name _____ Date _____

Factors, Multiples, and Arrays

Finding the Factors of 200

Find the factors of 200. Record the factors in the chart. You can use multiplication combinations you know to help you. You can also use the 200 chart, cubes, arrays, grid paper, or drawings to find the factors.

Factor	How Many in 200?	Factor Pair	Factor	How Many in 200?	Factor Pair

When you think you have found all of the factors of 200, list them here.

_____

_____

28 Unit 1   Session 3.1

▲ **Student Activity Book, p. 28**

Name _____ Date _____

Factors, Multiples, and Arrays

Finding the Factors of 300

Find the factors of 300. Record the factors in the chart. You can use multiplication combinations you know to help you. You can also use the 300 chart, cubes, arrays, grid paper, or drawings to find the factors.

Factor	How Many in 300?	Factor Pair	Factor	How Many in 300?	Factor Pair

When you think you have found all of the factors of 300, list them here.

_____

_____

Session 3.1   Unit 1 29

▲ **Student Activity Book, p. 29**

Use a transparency to introduce the 300 Chart as another tool students can use to help them find factors of larger numbers.

For the rest of the session, students find the factors of 200 and 300 and record them on *Student Activity Book* pages 28–29. Make available copies of the 300 Chart (M54) for their use. Tell students to keep the following questions in mind as they work:

- How can you use the factors of 100 to help you find the factors of 200 and 300?

- How can you use an array showing one pair of factors of a number to help you find other pairs of factors for that number?

- Are there numbers that you can eliminate, numbers that can't possibly be factors of 200 or of 300?

Let students know that they will continue working on the factors of these numbers and other multiples of 100 in the next session.

ONGOING ASSESSMENT: Observing Students at Work

Students use what they know about the factors of 100 and other multiplication relationships to find the factors of 300.

- **Are students using one factor they know to find its paired factor?** ("I knew that 25 is a factor of 200, and I counted 25, 50, 75, 100, 125, 150, 175, 200, so there are eight 25s, so 8 is another factor.")

- **Are students using what they know about factors of 100 to make conjectures about factors of 200 and 300?** ("I know that I can make an array of 100 with 10s, so I must be able to make an array for 200 with 10s because it would just be double the array for 100," or "If there are four 25s in 100, then there are four 25s in every 100, so there are four, eight, twelve 25s in 300.")

- **Do students reason by using number relationships to determine that some numbers cannot be factors of 200 and 300?** ("Any number larger than 150 can't be a factor of 300 because $2 \times 150 = 300$, and 2 times anything bigger would be more than 300.")

- **What representations do students use to help them find the factors of 200 and 300?** Do they skip count? If they are using other representations, such as arrays or cube models, do they need to actually construct these, or can they just visualize them?

- **Do students find all the factors of these numbers?**

SESSION FOLLOW-UP

Daily Practice and Homework

 Daily Practice: For ongoing review, have students complete *Student Activity Book* page 30.

 Homework: On *Student Activity Book* page 31, students find either missing factors or missing products in a set of multiplication combinations.

 Student Math Handbook: Students and families may use *Student Math Handbook* pages 24–25 for reference and review. See pages 134–139 in the back of this unit.

Name _____ Date _____

Factors, Multiples, and Arrays · Homework

More Factors and Products

Fill in the chart with the missing factors or products.

NOTE Students are working to become fluent with multiplication combinations (also called multiplication "facts"). Here, they solve problems to find a factor or products in some of the more difficult combinations.

SMH 26, 29–34

Factor	×	Factor	=	Product
10	×	9	=	
	×	7	=	77
12	×	8	=	
9	×		=	63
8	×	9	=	
	×	6	=	42
5	×	8	=	
6	×		=	48
4	×		=	36

Session 3.1 · Unit 1 **31**

▲ **Student Activity Book, p. 31**

▲ **Resource Masters, M54; T27**

Name _____ Date _____

Factors, Multiples, and Arrays

300 Chart

1	2	3	4	5	6	7	8	9	10
11	12	13	14	15	16	17	18	19	20
21	22	23	24	25	26	27	28	29	30
31	32	33	34	35	36	37	38	39	40
41	42	43	44	45	46	47	48	49	50
51	52	53	54	55	56	57	58	59	60
61	62	63	64	65	66	67	68	69	70
71	72	73	74	75	76	77	78	79	80
81	82	83	84	85	86	87	88	89	90
91	92	93	94	95	96	97	98	99	100
101	102	103	104	105	106	107	108	109	110
111	112	113	114	115	116	117	118	119	120
121	122	123	124	125	126	127	128	129	130
131	132	133	134	135	136	137	138	139	140
141	142	143	144	145	146	147	148	149	150
151	152	153	154	155	156	157	158	159	160
161	162	163	164	165	166	167	168	169	170
171	172	173	174	175	176	177	178	179	180
181	182	183	184	185	186	187	188	189	190
191	192	193	194	195	196	197	198	199	200
201	202	203	204	205	206	207	208	209	210
211	212	213	214	215	216	217	218	219	220
221	222	223	224	225	226	227	228	229	230
231	232	233	234	235	236	237	238	239	240
241	242	243	244	245	246	247	248	249	250
251	252	253	254	255	256	257	258	259	260
261	262	263	264	265	266	267	268	269	270
271	272	273	274	275	276	277	278	279	280
281	282	283	284	285	286	287	288	289	290
291	292	293	294	295	296	297	298	299	300

M54 · Unit 1 · Session 3.1

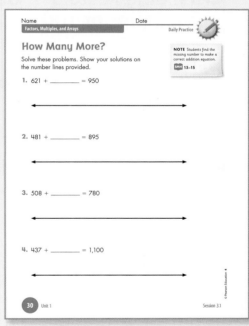

Name _____ Date _____

Factors, Multiples, and Arrays · Daily Practice

How Many More?

Solve these problems. Show your solutions on the number lines provided.

NOTE Students find the missing number to make a correct addition equation.

SMH 13–15

1. $621 + _____ = 950$

2. $481 + _____ = 895$

3. $508 + _____ = 780$

4. $437 + _____ = 1,100$

30 · Unit 1 · Session 3.1

▲ **Student Activity Book, p. 30**

Factors of the Multiples of 100

Math Focus Points

◆ Using knowledge of the factors of 100 to find factors of multiples of 100

◆ Using known multiplication combinations to find related multiplication combinations for a given product (e.g., if $4 \times 50 = 200$, then $8 \times 25 = 200$)

Today's Plan		Materials
① DISCUSSION **Strategies for Finding Factors of 200 and 300**	15 MIN CLASS	• *Student Activity Book,* pp. 28–29 (students' ongoing work)
② ACTIVITY **Finding Factors of Other Multiples of 100**	30 MIN PAIRS	• *Student Activity Book,* pp. 33–34 • M2; M53; M54 (from Session 3.1) • Connecting cubes or color tiles (as needed)
③ DISCUSSION **Finding Factors of Multiples of 100**	15 MIN CLASS	• Chart: "Ideas About Factors of Multiples of 100" • *Student Activity Book,* pp. 28–29, 33–34 (students' ongoing work)
④ SESSION FOLLOW-UP **Daily Practice and Homework**		• *Student Activity Book,* pp. 35–38 • *Student Math Handbook,* pp. 37–38

*See *Materials to Prepare,* p. 87.

Ten-Minute Math

Counting Around the Class Students count around the class by 20s. Each student says another multiple of 20 until all students have counted once. Highlight the multiples of 20 by writing them on the board as students say them.

How many students have counted at 180? 300? 420? What is a multiplication equation that would represent 7 people counting by 20s? ($7 \times 20 = 140$)

DISCUSSION

Strategies for Finding Factors of 200 and 300

15 MIN CLASS

Math Focus Points for Discussion

◆ Using knowledge of the factors of 100 to find factors of multiples of 100

◆ Using known multiplication combinations to find related multiplication combinations for a given product (e.g., if $4 \times 25 = 100$, then $8 \times 25 = 200$)

Begin this session by asking students to turn to *Student Activity Book* pages 28–29 and report on what they have found out so far about factors of 200 and 300. As students share their findings, list the factors on the board or overhead. You need not list all the factors if students have not yet found them all.❶ The goal of this discussion is to identify strategies for finding factors of a number by reasoning from known multiplication combinations.❷ Tell students that they will have time later in this session to find more factors of 200 and 300, as well as other multiples of 100.

Students might say:

"I used the factors of 100 to find the factors of 200 and 300."

"I think that if 25 is a factor of 100, it has to be a factor of 200 and 300."

Spend some time on these ideas:

How does knowing the factors of 100 help you with the factors of 200 and 300? Are all of the factors of 100, such as 25, also factors of 200 and 300? How can you convince us that this idea is true?

Encourage students to justify their ideas by referring to representations of multiplication they have used.

• How could you use arrays to explain more about the idea that a factor of 100 is also a factor of 200?

• Think of a story problem about 25s that would show that if 25 is a factor of 100, it is also a factor of 200.

• How could you use skip counting to explain this idea?

Teaching Note

❶ **Factors of 200 and 300** The complete list of factors is given in the discussion at the end of this session.

Differentiation

❷ **English Language Learners** In preparation for the discussion, consider previewing the material with a small group of English Language Learners. Ask them to tell you about the factors of 200 and 300. Provide a sentence-starting pattern to help students explain their ideas: "I know that _____, so _____." Practicing such explanations will help prepare English Language Learners for the End-of-Unit Assessment.

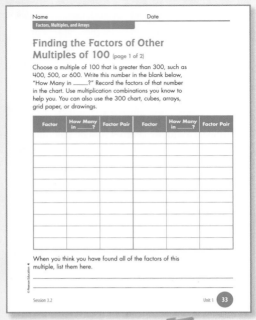

Name _____ Date _____
Factors, Multiples, and Arrays

Finding the Factors of Other
Multiples of 100 (page 1 of 2)

Choose a multiple of 100 that is greater than 300, such as
400, 500, or 600. Write this number in the blank below,
"How Many in _____?" Record the factors of that number
in the chart. Use multiplication combinations you know to
help you. You can also use the 300 chart, cubes, arrays,
grid paper, or drawings.

▲ Student Activity Book, p. 33

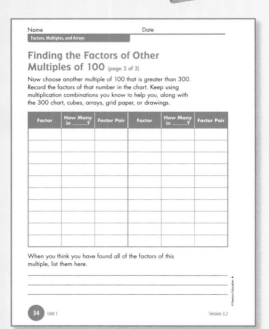

▲ Student Activity Book, p. 34

Keep in mind that discussion of this concept will continue at the end of this session, after students have had more time to find factors. Before sending students back to work, ask them about other strategies they used.

Were there any factors of 200 or 300 that were not factors of 100? How did you find those factors?

Students might say:

"150 is a factor of 300, but not of 100. I found it because 2 is a factor of 300, so 2 times something has to be 300. And it's 2 × 150."

Did anyone else look for pairs of factors? If you know that 50 is a factor of 300, then what other number must be a factor of 300? . . . What about 25? If 25 is a factor of 300, then what other number must also be a factor of 300?

"I know that 6 × 50 = 300. I found 12 × 25 by doubling the 6 and halving the 50."

[Marisol] used doubling and halving of one pair of factors to find another pair. Why do you think that works?

ACTIVITY

2 Finding Factors of Other Multiples of 100

30 MIN PAIRS

This activity provides an opportunity for students to work on multiplication problems with numbers that are larger than those they have encountered so far. The work on finding factors continues, with an emphasis on using what students know about the factors of 100 and extending this knowledge to multiples of 100.

Students who have yet to find all of the factors of 200 and 300 can continue looking for those and recording them on *Student Activity Book* pages 28–29. Other students can go on to locate factors of 400, 500, 600, or other multiples of 100 that they choose, recording them on *Student Activity Book* pages 33–34.

Remind students that they can use any available math tools, including the Factor Pairs for 100 chart.

Students might say:

"If I know 4 is a factor, then I think about what I can multiply 4 by to get to 300."

$$4 \times 25 = 100$$
$$4 \times 50 = 200$$
$$4 \times 75 = 300$$

Sample Student Work

"If 150 is a factor of 300, then half of 150 should work. It should fit twice as many times."

ONGOING ASSESSMENT: Observing Students at Work

Students use what they know about the factors of 100, about finding pairs of factors, and about reasoning from known multiplication combinations to find factors of 200, 300, and other multiples of 100.

- **Do students make deliberate choices about which numbers to try, on the basis of their knowledge of the relationship of 100 to its multiples?**

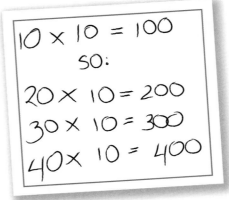

Sample Student Work

- **What representations do students use to help them find the factors of multiples of 100?** Do they skip count? If they are using other representations, such as arrays or connecting-cube models, do they need to actually construct these, or can they visualize them?

- **Do students find factors of multiples of 100 that are *not* factors of 100?** How do they find these?

- **Are students using a known factor to find its paired factor?** ("I know that 25 is a factor of 400, and there are four 25s in every hundred, so there are four, eight, twelve, sixteen 25s in 400; that means 16 is another factor of 400 because $25 \times 16 = 400$.")

- **Do students reason about number relationships to determine that some numbers cannot be factors of 200 and 300?** ("Any number larger than 150 can't be a factor of 300 because $2 \times 150 = 300$, and 2 times anything bigger would be more than 300.")

- **Do students think they need to try every number, or can they use what they know about multiplication relationships to eliminate some numbers as factors?** ("I didn't have to try any numbers between 200 and 300 for 600 because there are three 200s in 600, and there are two 300s in 600, and there is nothing between 2 and 3, so you can't have any other factor between 200 and 300 because there's nothing to multiply it by.")

DIFFERENTIATION: Supporting the Range of Learners

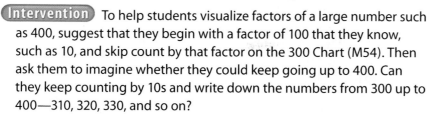

Intervention To help students visualize factors of a large number such as 400, suggest that they begin with a factor of 100 that they know, such as 10, and skip count by that factor on the 300 Chart (M54). Then ask them to imagine whether they could keep going up to 400. Can they keep counting by 10s and write down the numbers from 300 up to 400—310, 320, 330, and so on?

If students are having trouble generating factors of 300, suggest that they use 300 connecting cubes or tiles and see what rectangles they can make for 300.❸ They can work with one rectangle to generate others. For example, if they build a 10 × 30 rectangle, they might split that array into two 5 × 30 arrays and then rearrange them to make a 5 × 60 array, which gives them 2 more factors.

You can also ask students to sketch arrays on Centimeter Grid Paper (M2) to show how a factor of 100, such as 5, relates to 200 or 300. For example, students could draw two arrays of 20 × 5, as shown below, to represent 200.

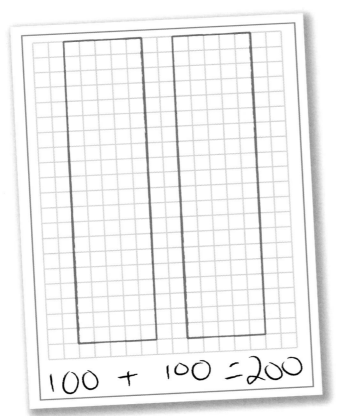

Ask questions such as these:

• How many 5s (or rows of 5) are in the first array? How many 5s are in 100?

Teaching Note

❸ **Number of Manipulatives** Even though 300 is a large number, fourth graders can manage this number of cubes, especially if you have the cubes stored in towers of 10.

Teaching Note

④ Identification of All Factors Fourth-grade students cannot be expected to know for certain when they have found all the factors of a larger number. At this point, the only foolproof method for most students would be to try every number between 1 and the given number. However, in this unit, the goal is to encourage students to reason from multiplication relationships they know to identify factors of a number. You can let pairs know when their list is complete, or tell them how many factors there are so that they can continue working on their lists.

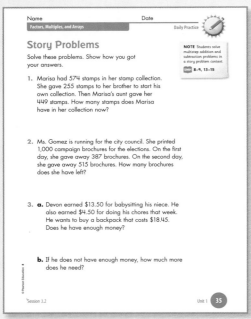

▲ Student Activity Book, p. 35

- Can you use this picture to figure out whether 5 is a factor of 200? Can you find how many 5s are in 200 to see whether there is another factor you can pair with 5?

Extension Students who can easily find factors of larger multiples of 100 could choose a multiple of 100 they would find challenging and try to find its factors, or they could work on the question, "When multiples of 100 get larger, do they have more factors? Why or why not?"

DISCUSSION

③ Finding Factors of Multiples of 100

15 MIN · CLASS

Math Focus Points for Discussion

◆ Using knowledge of the factors of 100 to find factors of multiples of 100

◆ Using known multiplication combinations to find related multiplication combinations for a given product (e.g., if $4 \times 50 = 200$, then $8 \times 25 = 200$)

Continue the discussion the class was having at the beginning of the session. Ask students what additional factors of 200 and 300 they found, and add them to your class list until all factors are included.④

Listing factors in pairs is helpful to students and can highlight a factor that students have not yet found. For example, if 20 has been listed as a factor of 300 but not 15, you can ask

What number would you need to multiply 20 by to get 300?

Factors of 200	Factors of 300
1 × 200	1 × 300
2 × 100	2 × 150
4 × 50	3 × 100
5 × 40	4 × 75
8 × 25	5 × 60
10 × 20	6 × 50
	10 × 30
	12 × 25
	15 × 20

Ask students which of the factors were the most difficult to find and what strategies helped them. For example, at first students often do not identify 8 as a factor of 200, but they find it when pairing it with 25 or when thinking of splitting a 4 × 50 array into two 4 × 25 arrays and recombining them to make an 8 × 25 array. ⑤

Then ask students what they noticed as they were finding factors of larger multiples of 100, such as 400 and 500. How did they find factors for these numbers? After hearing a few examples, ask:

- What general ideas has this activity given you?

- What do you see when you look at the factors you've found of different multiples of 100?

- Do you notice anything that would help you find factors of a new multiple of 100, such as 800 or 900?

Students sometimes make inaccurate generalizations. When this happens, pose questions for them to think about.

Students might say:

 "300 is the only hundreds number with 3 as a factor." ⑥

Could there be some other multiple of 100 that you haven't yet looked at that has 3 as a factor?

As student describe their methods, list them on the prepared chart, "Ideas About Factors of Multiples of 100." Keep this chart posted for Session 3.3. Suggestions may include ideas such as those shown in the sample chart on the following page.

Math Note

⑤ **Prime Factorization** One method of identifying all the factors of a number is prime factorization. The prime factorization of a number is the unique multiplication expression for that number that contains only prime numbers. For example, the prime factorization for 200 is $2 \times 2 \times 2 \times 5 \times 5$, and the prime factorization of 300 is $2 \times 2 \times 3 \times 5 \times 5$. By systematically listing all the numbers and all the combinations of numbers in the prime factorization (e.g., for 200: $2, 5, 2 \times 2, 2 \times 5, 2 \times 2 \times 2, 2 \times 2 \times 5$, and so on), it is possible to determine all the factors of that number.

Teaching Note

⑥ **Hundreds Numbers** Fourth graders often call the multiples of 100s "hundreds numbers."

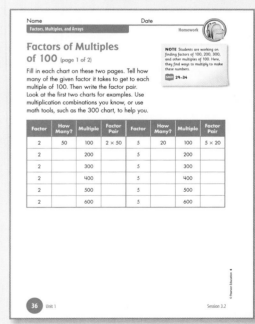

▲ Student Activity Book, p. 36

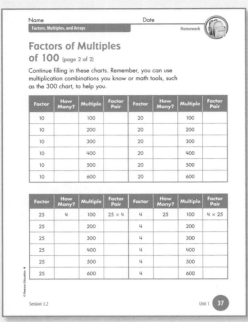

▲ Student Activity Book, p. 37

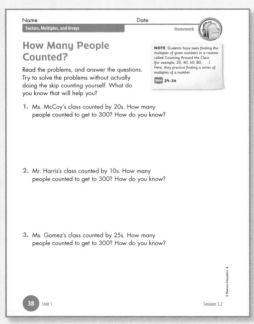

▲ Student Activity Book, p. 38

Ideas About Factors of Multiples of 100

The highest factor of a hundreds number is itself.

If you double factors of 100, you get factors of 200.

There are a lot of 5s in the factors of hundreds numbers. (5, 25, 50)

If you take the zeros off a hundreds number, you get one of its factors.

Hundreds numbers have a lot more even factors than odd ones.

300 has factors that the other hundreds numbers do not have. (3, 6, 12, 15, 30, 60, 75, 150, 300)

Every number has 1 and itself as factors.

SESSION FOLLOW-UP

4 Daily Practice and Homework

 Daily Practice: For ongoing review, have students complete *Student Activity Book* page 35.

Homework: For reinforcement of today's session, have students complete either *Student Activity Book* pages 36–37 or page 38.

Student Activity Book page 38 uses the context of *Counting Around the Class.* Tell students to try thinking about number relationships they know, rather than skip counting from the beginning. This homework is particularly useful for students who are still working on multiplication combinations for 200 and 300. You might lead them through an example that is not in the homework.

> If we were counting by 50s, how many people need to count to get to 300? How can you figure this out without counting by 50s?

 Student Math Handbook: Students and families may use *Student Math Handbook* pages 37–38 for reference and review. See pages 134–139 in the back of this unit.

Factors of Related Numbers

Math Focus Points

◆ Identifying the factors of a given number

◆ Using representations to show that a factor of a number is also a factor of its multiples (e.g., if 25 is a factor of 100, then 25 is also a factor of 300)

Today's Plan			Materials
ACTIVITY ① **Factors of 16 and 48**	35 MIN	PAIRS	• *Student Activity Book,* pp. 39–40 • M2* (from Session 3.1) • Color tiles or connecting cubes • Calculators (optional)
DISCUSSION ② **Are the Factors of 16 Also Factors of 48?**	25 MIN	CLASS	• *Student Activity Book,* pp. 39–40
SESSION FOLLOW-UP ③ **Daily Practice and Homework**			• *Student Activity Book,* pp. 41–42 • *Student Math Handbook,* p. 26

*See *Materials to Prepare,* p. 87.

Ten-Minute Math

Counting Around the Class Students count around the class by 100s. Each student says another multiple of 100 until all students have counted once. Highlight the multiples of 100 by writing them on the board as students say them.

How many students have counted at 1,000? 1,500? 2,000?

What is a multiplication equation that would represent 12 people counting by 100s?

($12 \times 100 = 1,200$)

ACTIVITY

1 Factors of 16 and 48

35 MIN   PAIRS

In this activity, students consider whether a factor of a number is always a factor of multiples of that number.

Yesterday, Nadeem and Ramona said that they thought that all the factors of 100 are also factors of 200 and 300, which are both multiples of 100. Then Lucy and Steve said that they thought this idea works for any multiple of 100.

Some of you noticed the same thing when we made arrays and found the factors of pairs of numbers, such as 25 and 50. You said that all the factors of 25 are also factors of 50, and 50 is a multiple of 25. So do you think this is always true, that the factors of any number are also factors of multiples of that number?

Take a few responses, and then introduce the activity.

Today we'll try out this idea with another pair of numbers that are not multiples of 100 and see what happens. [Write 16 and 48 on the board.] What can you tell me about the relationship between 16 and 48? Talk to a partner about this question.

Establish that 16 is a factor of 48, and make sure that students understand that $3 \times 16 = 48$. If needed, ask students how they could show that three 16s make 48. For example, sketch three 4×4 arrays, side by side.

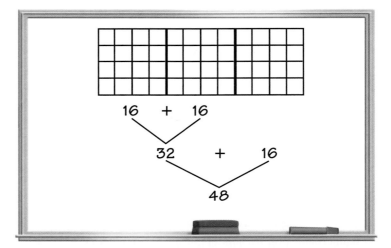

Ask students what all the factors of 16 are. Write their answers on the board until the list is complete (1, 2, 4, 8, 16).

This is today's question: Are all the factors of a number also factors of a *multiple* of that number? Think about these two numbers: 48 is a multiple of 16. Are all the factors of 16 also factors of 48?

Emphasize that you are looking for a convincing argument that addresses today's question.

I'm not looking for just a "yes" or "no" answer. I'm wondering why it's true or isn't true that factors of a number, such as 16, are also factors of a multiple of that number, such as 48. And will this be true for other numbers?

Have students work in pairs on *Student Activity Book* pages 39–40. Ask them to find a way to convince someone of their ideas, using a picture or representation that makes a convincing argument. Make available connecting cubes, color tiles, and grid paper.

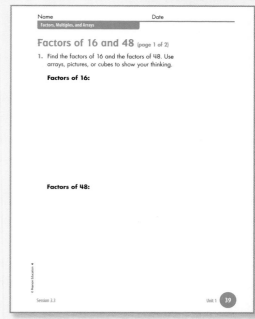

▲ **Student Activity Book, p. 39**

Students work to prove that all factors of a number are also factors of one of its multiples.

ONGOING ASSESSMENT: Observing Students at Work

Students find and represent the factors of 16 and 48, and then develop ways of showing or explaining why the factors of 16 are also factors of 48.

- **How do students find all the factors of both 16 and 48?** Do they use multiplication relationships they know? Do they use arrays, pictures, or connecting cubes to find the factors?

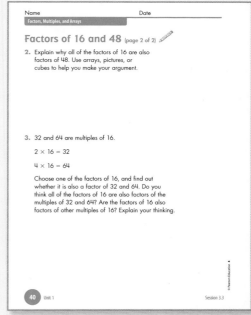

▲ **Student Activity Book, p. 40**

• **Do students recognize that a factor of 16 is also a factor of 48?**
Do they have a way of explaining or representing why this is true?
Support students as they look for a way to represent their thinking.
For example, if a student says, "If 2 fits into 16, then it has to fit into
the next 16 and the next 16," ask, "How could you show that with
cubes or tiles to help explain your idea to someone who doesn't
understand what you're saying?" Referring to a real or imagined
audience can be very helpful: "Suppose that Ms. Klein came in, and
she didn't know what we've been working on this week. How could
you convince her that a factor of 16 has to be a factor of 48, too?"

Ask students whose representations and explanations are most
effective to be prepared to share their work with the class.

DIFFERENTIATION: Supporting the Range of Learners

Extension If some students have developed a good explanation
and representation of why the factors of 16 are also factors of 48, ask
them to show how their idea works with 96.

DISCUSSION

2 Are the Factors of 16 Also Factors of 48?

25 MIN CLASS

Math Focus Points for Discussion

◆ Using representations to show that a factor of a number is also a factor
of its multiples (e.g., if 25 is a factor of 100, then 25 is also a factor of 300)

Many of you noticed that all the factors of 16 (1, 2, 4, 8, and 16) are
also factors of 48. Let's talk about why that is true.

Ask two or three students to share their representations of why a factor
of 16, such as 4, is also a factor of 48.

Students might say:

"I made three 4 × 4 arrays and put them together to make a 12 × 4 array, which is 48. 16 fits into 48 three times, and 4 fits into each of the 16s. There are four 4s in each one, and I know 3 × 4 = 12, so 4 will fit into 48 twelve times."

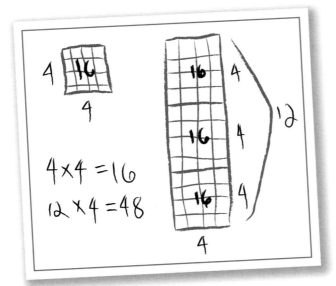

Sample Student Work

"See—there are 4s in every 16. If you can split one of the 16s into 4s, then you can split all of the 16s into 4s. It doesn't matter how many 16s you have, you can just keep splitting them into 4s."

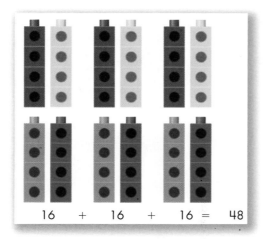

Algebra Note

❶ **Factors and Multiples** For more about how fourth graders make sense of the way a factor of a number is related to multiples of that number, see "Finding Factors" in *Algebra Connections in This Unit,* page 17.

Everyone seems pretty convinced that all the factors of 16 are also factors of 48. What about other multiples of 16? For example, how many is four 16s? *(64)* Do you think *all* the factors of 16 are also factors of 64? Can you draw or make something to convince us that that's true, so we don't have to try out each factor of 16?

Collect students' responses to these questions, based on their work on Question 3 on *Student Activity Book* page 40.

Do you think this is always true? Will the factors of any number be factors of all the multiples of that number?

If you have additional time, students can continue to try out this idea with numbers that they choose.❶

DIFFERENTIATION: Supporting the Range of Learners

Intervention Expect a range of understanding about the more general idea that a factor of any number is also a factor of its multiples. Some students will be able to generalize about factors and multiples, given any pair of related numbers. Others will be able to explain their ideas only for particular pairs of numbers.

By continuing to work on other pairs of numbers, you can help these students begin to grasp the greater concept as they notice similarities in how to prove that factors of one number are automatically factors of its multiples. For example, 3 is a factor of 6. Is it a factor of all the multiples of 6?

Some students may notice the following: If 6 is a factor of a number, 3 is also a factor of that number, yet the reverse is not necessarily true. If 3 is a factor of a number, 6 is not necessarily a factor of that number. For example, 3 is a factor of 33, but 6 is not.

SESSION FOLLOW-UP

Daily Practice and Homework

 Daily Practice: For ongoing review, have students complete *Student Activity Book* page 41.

 Homework: On *Student Activity Book* page 42, students solve groups of related problems that all involve factors of 100. This continues the work of looking for relationships among factors and multiples.

 Student Math Handbook: Students and families may use *Student Math Handbook* page 26 for reference and review. See pages 134–139 in the back of this unit.

Name _____ Date _____

Factors, Multiples, and Arrays   Daily Practice

Combinations to 100 and 200

NOTE Students use number sense and place-value knowledge to solve addition problems.

1. | 4 | 9 | 2 | 7 | 6 | 3 |

☐☐ + ☐☐ = _____

Use this set of digits to write an equation that will be as close to 100 as possible. Use 2-digit numbers in your equation. Explain why this is as close to 100 as you can get with this set of digits.

2. | 4 | 9 | 2 | 7 | 6 | 3 | 5 | 1 |

☐☐ + ☐☐ + ☐☐ = _____

Use this set of digits to write an equation that will be as close to 200 as possible. Use three 2-digit numbers in your equation. Explain why this is as close to 200 as you can get with this set of digits.

Session 3.3   Unit 1 **41**

▲ **Student Activity Book, p. 41**

Name _____ Date _____

Factors, Multiples, and Arrays   Homework

Multiplying by Factors of 100

NOTE Students have been finding factors of 100, 200, and 300. Here, they solve multiplication problems that involve these factors.

SMH 37, 38

Solve each set of problems. Look for patterns that might help you.

1. $2 \times 50 =$ _____	2. $4 \times 25 =$ _____
$4 \times 50 =$ _____	$6 \times 25 =$ _____
$6 \times 50 =$ _____	$8 \times 25 =$ _____
3. _____ $\times 4 = 100$	4. $10 \times$ _____ $= 200$
_____ $\times 4 = 200$	$10 \times$ _____ $= 300$
_____ $\times 4 = 300$	$10 \times$ _____ $= 400$
5. $5 \times 20 =$ _____	6. _____ $\times 5 = 100$
$10 \times 20 =$ _____	_____ $\times 5 = 200$
$15 \times 20 =$ _____	_____ $\times 5 = 400$

42 Unit 1   Session 3.3

▲ **Student Activity Book, p. 42**

End-of-Unit Assessment

Math Focus Points

◆ Using arrays to model multiplication situations

◆ Using arrays to find factors of 2-digit numbers

◆ Using known multiplication combinations to determine the products of more difficult combinations

Today's Plan		Materials
ASSESSMENT ACTIVITY **1** **End-of-Unit Assessment**	✓ 🕐 60 MIN 👤 INDIVIDUALS	• M55–M56*
SESSION FOLLOW-UP **2** **Daily Practice**		• *Student Activity Book*, p. 43 • *Student Math Handbook*, p. 23

*See *Materials to Prepare*, p. 87.

Ten-Minute Math

Counting Around the Class Students count around the class by 50s. Each student says another multiple of 50 until all students have counted once. Highlight the multiples of 50 by writing them on the board as students say them.

How many students have counted at 400? 550? 850?

What is a multiplication equation that would represent 13 people counting by 50s?

$(13 \times 50 = 650)$

ASSESSMENT ACTIVITY
End-of-Unit Assessment

60 MIN | **INDIVIDUALS**

This End-of-Unit Assessment (M55–M56) addresses the three benchmarks for this unit.❶

- In Problem 1, Part A, students are asked to solve a multiplication problem (6 × 9). This addresses Benchmark 1: Use known multiplication combinations to find the product of any multiplication combination up to 12 × 12.

- In Problem 1, Parts B and C, students are asked to create both a visual image and a story context to represent the multiplication problem 6 × 9. This addresses Benchmark 2: Use arrays, pictures or models of groups, and story contexts to represent multiplication situations.

- In Problem 2, students are asked to find and represent all the factors of 36. This addresses Benchmark 3: Find the factors of 2-digit numbers.

For each problem, some students may need help understanding what is being asked. Support these students by asking them to talk the problem through with you. Other students may need help putting their thinking on paper so that it can be easily understood. Ask them to explain their thinking aloud so that you can help them choose words, mathematical expressions, and images to put their thoughts in writing.

Students might use grid paper for their work on Problem 2, finding all the factors of 36.

Professional Development

❶ **Teacher Note:** End-of-Unit Assessment, p. 123

Name _____ Date _____

Factors, Multiples, and Arrays

End-of-Unit Assessment (page 1 of 2)

Problem 1

A. Solve this multiplication combination.

$$6 \times 9 =$$

Did you use another multiplication combination to help you get the answer? If you did, explain what combination you used and how it helped you find the product of 6 × 9.

_____
_____
_____

B. Draw a picture of either arrays, objects, or cubes to show that your answer is correct.

C. Write a story to go with the problem 6 × 9.

_____
_____
_____
_____
_____
_____

Session 3.4   Unit 1 **M55**

▲ **Resource Masters, M55** *PORTFOLIO*

Name _____ Date _____

Factors, Multiples, and Arrays

End-of-Unit Assessment (page 2 of 2)

Problem 2

You have 36 cans of juice.

A. Show all the ways you can arrange these cans into arrays. You may either draw arrays in the space below or use grid paper.

B. List all the factors of 36.

M56 Unit 1   Session 3.4

▲ **Resource Masters, M56** *PORTFOLIO*

▲ **Student Activity Book, p. 43**

Most students will not need the entire 60 minutes to complete this assessment. When they finish, suggest that they quietly return to activities from previous sessions in this unit, such as Finding Factors of Other Multiples of 100 (*Student Activity Book* pages 33–34), or the game *Multiple Turn Over* (M45).

SESSION FOLLOW-UP
2 Daily Practice

Daily Practice: For enrichment, have students complete *Student Activity Book* page 43. This page provides real-world problems involving the math content of this unit.

Student Math Handbook: Students and families may use *Student Math Handbook* page 23 for reference and review. See pages 134–139 in the back of this unit.

Factors, Multiples, and Arrays

In Part 6 of *Implementing Investigations in Grade 4,* you will find a set of Teacher Notes that addresses topics and issues applicable to the curriculum as a whole rather than to specific curriculum units. They include the following:

Computational Fluency and Place Value

Computational Algorithms and Methods

Representations and Contexts for Mathematical Work

Foundations of Algebra in the Elementary Grades

Discussing Mathematical Ideas

Racial and Linguistic Diversity in the Classroom:
    What Does Equity Mean in Today's Math Classroom?

Images of Multiplication

It is important that students develop strong visual images of multiplication as they develop strategies for solving multiplication problems. If students can visualize clearly how the numbers they are multiplying are related, they can develop flexible, efficient, and accurate strategies for solving multiplication problems.

Students encountered many ways to represent multiplication in Grade 3 that they will continue to use in Grade 4—pictures of groups of things in a story context, skip counting on a 100 chart, and arrays. As students work with larger numbers in Grade 4, it becomes cumbersome to draw pictures, skip count on a large number chart, or use arrays with all the individual units shown. Students need to learn to visualize these representations mentally to help them break up the numbers and keep track of which parts of the problem have been solved and which remain to be solved.

As you work with students, suggest these ways of visualizing multiplication, especially when a student cannot figure out where to start or when a student has solved part of a problem and is unsure how to continue.

Images of Equal Groups in a Story Context

Most students can represent a multiplication expression such as 6 × 4 by creating a picture similar to this one:

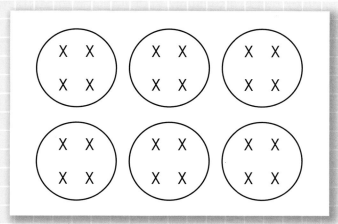

Ask students to generate simple stories that help them visualize a multiplication expression such as 6 × 4 as equal groups (e.g., 6 bags with 4 marbles in each bag). Help students select simple contexts that are familiar to them. Then you can ask students to imagine that context as a way of thinking through the problem. In Grades 3 and 4, students are moving away from thinking of multiplication as repeated addition. Instead of adding up 4s, students can be encouraged to use the image to start with a larger chunk of the problem. For example, you might ask, "Can you visualize how many marbles would be in 2 bags? In 3 bags? . . . Now how many more bags of 4 are there?" A story context involving equal groups can help students use what they know to determine the product: "I know that there are 12 marbles in 3 of the bags—oh, so there's 3 more bags, so I double that to get 24."

Representing Multiplication as Skip Counting

In Grade 3, students spent time creating and understanding skip counting charts. On 100 charts, students marked off multiples of the numbers 2 through 12.

1	2	3	4	5	6	7	8	9	10
11	12	13	14	15	16	17	18	19	20
21	22	23	24	25	26	27	28	29	30
31	32	33	34	35	36	37	38	39	40
41	42	43	44	45	46	47	48	49	50
51	52	53	54	55	56	57	58	59	60
61	62	63	64	65	66	67	68	69	70
71	72	73	74	75	76	77	78	79	80
81	82	83	84	85	86	87	88	89	90
91	92	93	94	95	96	97	98	99	100

These charts provided an opportunity for students to notice patterns in each number's multiples and to consider the relationship between multiples of various numbers. Ask students questions that help them visualize the counting number sequence and think through how to calculate the next multiple as they are skip counting.

Representing Multiplication with Arrays

In this unit, students work with Array Cards and drawings in which all the individual units of the array are visible. These arrays are a representation of the groups and amounts in a group in any multiplication problem.

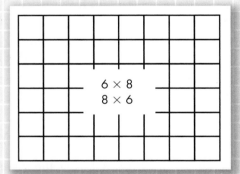

This 6×8 array can be seen as 8 groups of 6 items or as 6 groups of 8 items. In either case, students can visualize the problem as a whole and then visualize the smaller parts that may help them find the product. For example, if juice boxes come in sets of 6, a student might think of 8×6 as 8 sets of juice boxes. The student could visualize these in an array and use that image to break the problem into parts that are easier to solve, as follows:

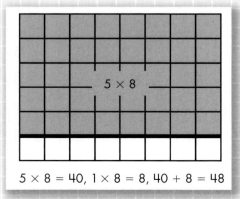

The story problems in Investigations 1 and 2 and the *Quick Images* activity that is introduced in this unit (page 59) also provide experience with arrays that represent multiplication situations. For example, *Student Activity Book* page 1 shows cans in a 6×8 array. The *Quick Images* in this unit show combinations of arrays that provide the opportunity to describe a product in different ways. For example, *Quick Image* 7 might be described as 6×4 (6 rows of 4 dots), 8×3 (8 groups of vertical rows of 3 dots each), 2×12 (2 rectangles, each with 12 dots), or even $2 \times 3 \times 4$ (2 rectangles, each with 3 rows of 4 dots).

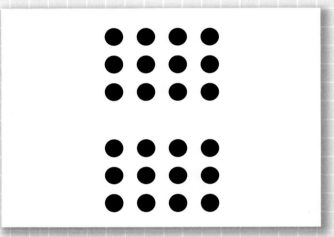

Visualizing how to break multiplication problems into parts becomes even more important as students solve multidigit problems in *Multiple Towers and Division Stories* and *How Many Packages? How Many Groups?* See **Teacher Note:** Representing Multiplication with Arrays (page 117), for more information about how arrays are used in this unit and how the use of arrays can be extended to represent more difficult multiplication and division problems. In the next unit on multiplication and division, *Multiple Towers and Division Stories,* the **Teacher Note:** Visualizing Arrays provides information about how and why students make a transition from using arrays marked with individual units to visualizing unmarked arrays.

Representing Multiplication with Arrays

Representing mathematical relationships is a key element of developing mathematical understanding. For multiplication, the rectangular array is an important tool. It meets all the criteria for a powerful mathematical representation: it highlights important relationships, provides a tool for solving problems, and can be extended as students apply ideas about multiplication in new areas.

Why Arrays for Multiplication?

As students come to understand the operation of multiplication in Grades 3 and 4, they gradually move away from thinking of multiplication as only repeated addition. They learn that multiplication has particular properties that distinguish it from addition. Although a number line or 100 chart can be used to show how multiplication can be viewed as adding equal groups, neither of these tools provides easy access to other important properties of multiplication. The rectangular array provides a window into properties that are central to students' work in learning the multiplication combinations and in solving multidigit multiplication and division problems.

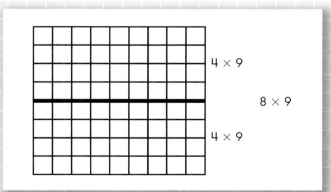

Here is an example—working on 8×9, one of the more difficult multiplication combinations for most students—of how an array can illustrate that $8 \times 9 = (4 \times 9) + (4 \times 9)$. In splitting a multiplication problem such as 8×9 into sub problems $[(4 \times 9) + (4 \times 9)]$, you are using the distributive property. The number that you break up is distributed into parts that must all be multiplied by the other number. This property of multiplication is at the core of almost all common strategies used to solve multiplication problems.

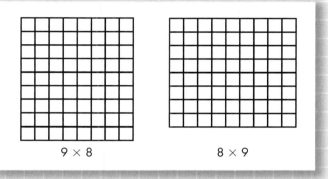

The rectangular array also makes it clearer why the product of 9×8 is the same as the product of 8×9. The array can be rotated to show that 9 rows with 8 in each row have the same number of squares as 8 rows with 9 in each row. The column on one becomes the row on the other, illustrating the commutative property—the fact that you can change the order of the factors in a multiplication equation without changing the product.

Arrays are particularly useful for solving or visualizing how to solve multidigit multiplication problems. After students have worked with rectangular arrays for single-digit multiplication combinations and thoroughly understand how an array represents the factors and product, they can use arrays in their work to solve harder problems later in Grade 4. For example, the array for 28 × 25 can be broken up in many ways, as follows:

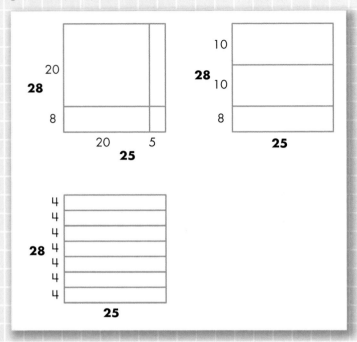

Arrays also support students' learning about the relationship between multiplication and division. In a division problem such as 176 ÷ 8, the dividend (176) is represented by the number of squares in the array, and the divisor (8) is one dimension of the array.

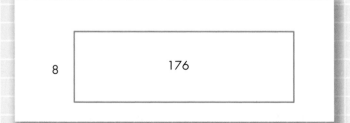

Students can think of "slicing off" pieces of the rectangle as they gradually figure out the other factor:

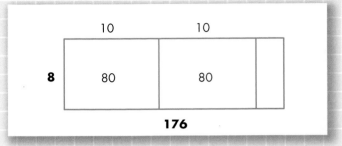

Finally, the use of the rectangular array can be extended in later grades as students work with multiplication of fractions and, later, of algebraic expressions.

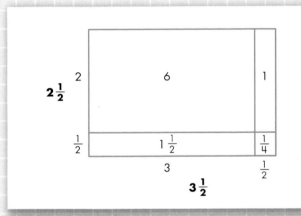

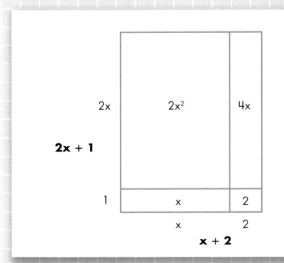

For multiplication notation to describe arrays, the *Investigations* curriculum uses the convention of designating the number of rows first and the number in each row second; for example, 3 × 2 indicates 3 rows with 2 in each row.

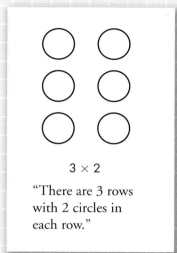

3 × 2

"There are 3 rows with 2 circles in each row."

This convention is consistent with using 3 × 2 to indicate 3 groups of 2 in other multiplication situations (e.g., 3 pots with 2 flowers in each pot). However, at this age level, it is not necessary for students to follow this system rigidly; trying to remember which number stands for rows and which for the number in a row can be unnecessarily distracting for students.

When students suggest a multiplication expression for an array, what is important is that they understand what the numbers mean; for example, a student might show how 3 × 2 represents 3 rows of cans with 2 in each row or 3 cans in each of 2 rows.

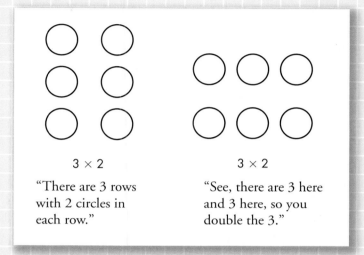

3 × 2

"There are 3 rows with 2 circles in each row."

3 × 2

"See, there are 3 here and 3 here, so you double the 3."

Note that in other cultures, conventions about interpreting multiplication expressions differ. In some countries, the convention for interpreting 3 × 2 is not "3 groups of 2" but "3 taken 2 times."

Learning and Assessing Multiplication Combinations

In Investigation 2 of this unit, students review the multiplication combinations they worked on in Grade 3 (combinations with products to 50) and then work on the rest of the multiplication combinations to 12×12 so that they become fluent with all of them. Students are expected to know the multiplication combinations fluently by the middle of Grade 4 (see the list of benchmarks by grade level at the end of this Teacher Note).

Although there is some time built into Investigation 2 to work on the multiplication combinations, many students will need additional practice during this unit and after this unit is completed. You can use Multiplication Combinations (M51) as well as the Multiplication Cards (M35–M40) for this practice. With your guidance about which multiplication combinations to work on, students should continue learning these combinations at home or outside of math time. You may have other favorite practice methods or activities that you want to suggest for particular students. Also, enlist the help of parents or other family members. This Teacher Note provides recommendations for supporting students in their ongoing practice.

Why Do We Call Them *Combinations*?

The pairs of factors from 1×1 through 12×12 are traditionally referred to as "multiplication facts"—those multiplication combinations with which students are expected to be fluent. The *Investigations* curriculum follows the National Council of Teachers of Mathematics (NCTM) convention of calling these expressions *combinations* rather than *facts*. *Investigations* does this for two reasons. First, naming *only* particular addition and multiplication combinations as *facts* seems to give them elevated status, more important than other critical parts of mathematics. In addition, the word *fact* implies that something cannot be learned through reasoning. For example, it is a fact that the first president of the United States was George Washington,

and it is a fact that Rosa Parks was born in Alabama in 1913. If these facts are important for us to know, we can remember them or use reference materials to look them up. However, the product for the multiplication combination 6×7 can be determined in many ways; it is logically connected to our system of numbers and operations. If we forget the product, but understand what multiplication is and know some related multiplication combinations, we can find the product through reasoning. For example, if we know that $5 \times 7 = 35$, we can add one more 7 to determine that the product of 6×7 is 42. If we know that $3 \times 7 = 21$, we can reason that the product of 6×7 would be twice that, $2 \times (3 \times 7) = 42$.

The term *facts* does convey a meaning that is generally understood by some students and family members, so you will need to decide whether to use the term *facts* along with *combinations* in certain settings in order to make your meaning clear.

Fluency with Multiplication Combinations

Like NCTM, this curriculum supports the importance of students learning the basic combinations through a focus on reasoning about number relationships: "Fluency with whole-number computation depends, in large part, on fluency with basic number combinations—the single digit addition and multiplication pairs and their counterparts for subtraction and division. Fluency with basic number combinations develops from well-understood meanings for the four operations and from a focus on thinking strategies. . . ." (*Principles and Standards for School Mathematics*, pages 152–153)

Fluency means that combinations are quickly accessible mentally, either because they are immediately known or because the calculation that is used is so effortless as to be essentially automatic (in the way that some adults quickly derive one combination from another).

Helping Students Learn the Multiplication Combinations

A. Students Who Know Their Combinations to 50

Students who know their combinations to 50, as well as the combinations that involve multiplying by 10 up to 100 ($6 \times 10, 7 \times 10, 8 \times 10, 9 \times 10, 10 \times 10$), can work on learning the most difficult combinations. Here is one way of sequencing this work.

1. Learning the remaining combinations with products to 100.
There are 6 difficult facts to learn (other than the $\times 11$ and $\times 12$ combinations, which are, in fact, not as difficult as these, and are discussed below). These six difficult combinations are: 6×9 (and 9×6), 7×8 (and 8×7), 7×9 (and 9×7), 8×8, 8×9 (and 9×8), and 9×9. Note that knowing that multiplication is commutative is crucial for learning all the multiplication combinations. The work with Array Cards supports this understanding, see **Teacher Note:** Representing Multiplication with Arrays, page 117.

Students can work on one or two of these most difficult multiplication combinations each week. Make sure that they use combinations they do know to help them learn ones they don't know—for example, $8 \times 7 = 2 \times (4 \times 7)$, or $9 \times 7 = (10 \times 7) - 7$. They can write these related multiplication combinations as "start with" hints on the Multiplication Cards. If most of your class needs to work on the same few hard combinations, you might want to assign the whole class to focus on two of these each week.

2. Learning the ×11 and ×12 combinations.
We consider these combinations to be in a different category. Historically, these combinations were included in the list of "multiplication facts." However, when we are dealing with 2-digit numbers in multiplication, an efficient way to solve them is through applying the distributive property, breaking the numbers apart by place as you would with any other 2-digit numbers. We include them here because some local or state frameworks still require knowing multiplication combinations through 12×12. In addition, 12 is a number that occurs often in our culture, and it is useful to know the $\times 12$ combinations fluently. Most students learn the $\times 11$ combinations easily because of the pattern (11, 22, 33, 44, 55, . . .) created by multiplying successive whole numbers by 11. They should also think through why this pattern occurs: $3 \times 11 = (3 \times 10) + (3 \times 1) = 30 + 3 = 33$. They should think through why $11 \times 10 = 110$ and $11 \times 11 = 121$ by breaking up the numbers. Students can learn the $\times 12$ combinations by breaking the 12 into a 10 and 2, e.g., $12 \times 6 = (10 \times 6) + (2 \times 6)$. Some students may also want to use doubling or adding on to known combinations: $12 \times 6 = 2 \times (6 \times 6)$, or $12 \times 6 = (11 \times 6) + 6$.

B. Students Who Need Review and Practice of Combinations to 50

Students who have difficulty learning the multiplication combinations often view this task as overwhelming—an endless mass of combinations with no order and reason. Bringing order and reason to students' learning of these combinations in a way that lets them have control over their progress is essential. Traditionally, students learned one "table" at a time (e.g., first the $\times 2$ combinations, then the $\times 3$ combinations, the $\times 4$ combinations, and so on). However, the multiplication combinations can be grouped in other ways to support learning related combinations.

First, make sure that students know all multiplication combinations that involve $\times 0, \times 1, \times 2, \times 5$, and $\times 10$ (up to 10×10) fluently. (Students worked with the $\times 0$ combinations in Grade 3.) Note that, although most fourth graders can easily count by 2, 5, and 10, the student who is fluent does not need to skip count to determine the product of multiplication combinations involving these numbers.

When students know these combinations, turn to those that they have not yet learned. Provide a sequence of small groups of combinations that students can relate to what they already know. There are a number of ways to do this.

1. Learning the ×4 combinations.
Work on the $\times 4$ combinations that students do not yet know: $3 \times 4, 4 \times 4, 6 \times 4, 7 \times 4, 8 \times 4$, and 9×4. Help students think of these as doubling the $\times 2$ combinations. So, $4 \times 6 = (2 \times 6) + (2 \times 6)$, or $4 \times 6 = 2 \times (2 \times 6)$. Students may verbalize this idea as "4 times 6 is 2 times 6 and

another 2 times 6," or "to get 4 times 6, I double 2×6." Doubling is also useful within the $\times 4$ combinations; for example, when students know that $3 \times 4 = 12$, then that fact can be used to solve 6×4: $6 \times 4 = (3 \times 4) + (3 \times 4)$. Getting used to thinking about doubling with smaller numbers will also prepare students for using this approach with some of the harder combinations.

2. Learning the square numbers. Next, students learn or review the four remaining combinations that produce square numbers less than 50: 3×3, 5×5, 6×6, and 7×7. These are often easy for students to remember. If needed, use doubling or a known combination for "start with" clues during practice (e.g., 6×6 is double 3×6; 5×5 is 5 more than 4×5). Students can also build these combinations with tiles or draw them on grid paper to see how they can be represented by squares.

3. Learning the remaining combinations with products to 50. Finally, learn or review the six remaining combinations with products to 50: 3×6 through 3×9, 7×6, and 8×6. First, relate them to known combinations (e.g., double 3×3 or halve 6×6 to get 3×6), and then practice them.

Assessing Students' Knowledge of Multiplication Combinations

Over the next few months, do some periodic assessment to help you and your students keep track of which multiplication combinations they know fluently and which they still need to practice.

In the second multiplication and division unit of Grade 4, *Multiple Towers and Division Stories*, students will have a final check of their fluency with multiplication combinations and begin to work on their division counterparts. Work on these related division problems will continue in the last Grade 4 multiplication and division unit, *How Many Packages? How Many Groups?* In the meantime, as students work on division problems, help them relate division expressions to the multiplication combinations they know: "What multiplication combination can help you solve $24 \div 6$?"

Fluency Benchmarks for Learning Combinations Through the Grades

Addition: fluent by end of Grade 2, with review and practice in Grade 3

Subtraction: fluent by end of Grade 3, with review and practice in Grade 4

Multiplication: fluent with multiplication combinations with products to 50 by the end of Grade 3; up to 12×12 by the middle of Grade 4, with continued review and practice

Division: fluent by end of Grade 5

End-of-Unit Assessment

Problem 1 Part A

Benchmark addressed:

Benchmark 1: Use known multiplication combinations to find the product of any multiplication combination up to 12×12.

In order to meet the benchmark, students' work should show that they can:

- Demonstrate knowledge of the multiplication combination 6×9 or the ability to derive the product of this combination from known multiplication combinations;

- Show how they solved the problem.

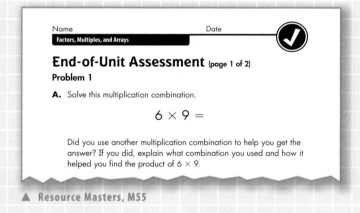

Name _____ Date _____ ✓

Factors, Multiples, and Arrays

End-of-Unit Assessment (page 1 of 2)

Problem 1

A. Solve this multiplication combination.

$$6 \times 9 =$$

Did you use another multiplication combination to help you get the answer? If you did, explain what combination you used and how it helped you find the product of 6×9.

▲ **Resource Masters, M55**

Meeting the Benchmark

The following examples of student work provide a range of typical responses. All of these students met the benchmark—they were able to interpret the problem and solve it accurately.

Anna used known multiplication combinations to derive the product of 6×9 and demonstrated an understanding

of 6×9 as the sum of the products of 6×6 and 6×3. She wrote:

"For a short cut, I did 6×6 to get me to 36. So then after that I just had to do 6×3 because $3 + 6 = 9$. $6 \times 3 = 18$, so then I added the totals together to get 54. $36 + 18 = 54$."

Derek used his understanding of the relationship between 3 groups of 9 and 6 groups of 9 to find the product of 6×9. He wrote:

"I know that 3×9 is 27. I know that 3 is half of 6, so 6×9 is 54. $27 + 27 = 54$."

Noemi used knowledge of the $\times 10$ combinations to solve this problem. She wrote:

"I know that $6 \times 10 = 60$. Then I had to take away one 6 because the problem is really 6×9. $60 - 6 = 54$."

At this point in Grade 4, some students will know the product of 6×9 without having to derive it from a simpler combination.

Partially Meeting the Benchmark

Some students understand the structure of the problem but make computational errors. For example, they may incorrectly combine the products of the multiplication combinations they used to derive the product of 6×9. After you review their assessments, ask these students to double-check their work. For example: "I see that you used $4 \times 9 = 36$ and $2 \times 9 = 18$ to find the product of 6×9. Your paper says that $36 + 18 = 53$. How could you double-check that?"

Encourage these students to take their time and work carefully to avoid such errors in the future. In addition, note whether these kinds of errors are consistent across problems or more of a one-time occurrence.

Not Meeting the Benchmark

These students do not accurately find the product of 6 × 9 and fail to use known combinations to help them. Ask questions to help them think about related combinations they might know. For example: "Can you tell me what 2 × 9 equals? Can this help you find the answer to 6 × 9?"

Problem 1 Parts B and C

Benchmark addressed:

Benchmark 2: Use arrays, pictures or models of groups, and story contexts to represent multiplication situations.

In order to meet the benchmark, students' work should show that they can:

- Draw a representation of 6 × 9 that demonstrates their understanding of this expression as representing 6 groups of 9 or 9 groups of 6 and shows that the product of this combination is 54;

- Interpret the task as writing a story problem involving 6 groups of 9 or 9 groups of 6, including a question or a statement about the product.

B. Draw a picture of either arrays, objects, or cubes to show that your answer is correct.

C. Write a story to go with the problem 6 × 9.

_____
_____
_____
_____
_____
_____
_____

Session 3.4   Unit 1 **M55**

© Pearson Education 4

▲ Resource Masters, M55

Meeting the Benchmark

The following examples of student work provide a range of typical responses. Both of these students met the benchmark—they were able to represent the meaning of the expression 6 × 9 and show why the product of this combination is 54. They were also able to write story problems involving 6 groups of 9 or 9 groups of 6 and include a question or statement about the product of 6 × 9.

Enrique drew a 6 × 9 array and counted by 6 to label each column.

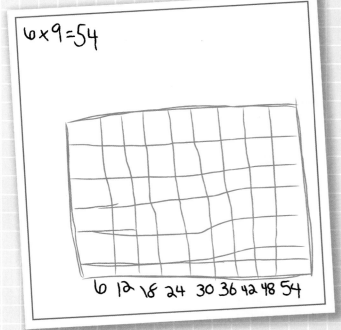

6×9=54

6 12 18 24 30 36 42 48 54

Enrique's Work

He wrote:

"I had 9 packs of juice. In each pack there were 6 boxes. Altogether, I had 54 boxes of juice."

Lucy drew six apple trees with 9 apples on each tree, grouped the 9s to make three 18s, added two of the 18s to make 36, and added the final 18 to make 54.

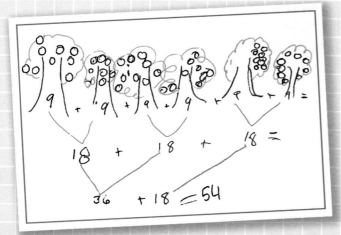

Lucy's Work

She wrote:

"There are 6 trees. Each tree has nine apples. How many apples are there altogether?

Partially Meeting the Benchmark

These students have completed part of the task successfully. They may have drawn a correct representation of 6 × 9 but failed to show why the product of this combination is 54. Ask these students how they could prove to you that there are 54 objects in their representation. Other students, as in the examples below, may have drawn accurate representations of 6 × 9 but failed to write a complete and/or accurate story problem.

Amelia's representation correctly showed 6 groups of 9 and demonstrated that the product of 6 × 9 is 54. She drew the following representation, showing 6 groups of 9 cubes and skip counted by 9 to show the product.

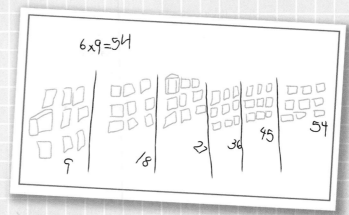

Amelia's Work

However, the story problem she wrote ("There were 6 groups of people. They each had 9 papers. How many people are there?") demonstrates confusion about the meaning of the numbers in the problem.

Ask students such as Amelia to read the story problem they wrote out loud to see whether they self-correct. If they do not see their error, ask questions to help them focus on the meaning of each number. Ask them to draw a picture showing what they mean. For example: "What does the 6 mean in your story? Show me a picture of what you mean. Tell me in your own words what is happening in your story."

Jake drew a 9 × 6 array of dots and grouped the dots into 4 groups of 12 and 1 group of 6 as seen below.

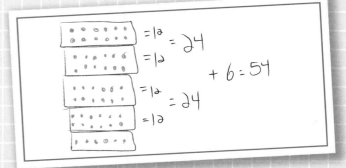

Jake's Work

Jake found the correct product, but he wrote:

"There are 6 beds: 9 people in each bed."

Ask students such as Jake whether they think that the story problem is complete. For example: "I see you wrote about 6 beds with 9 people in each one. What piece of information do we not know about this multiplication situation? What question could you ask about your problem?"

Not Meeting the Benchmark

These students are unsuccessful in making a representation or writing a story problem for 6 × 9 that demonstrates an understanding of the expression as representing 6 groups of 9 or 9 groups of 6. Sketch a representation of a simpler combination for these students, and ask them what equation they could write to describe what you drew. For example: "What do you see in the picture I just drew? What equation could I write to go with this picture?"

Problem 2

Benchmark addressed:

Benchmark 3: Find the factors of 2-digit numbers.

In order to meet the benchmark, students' work should show that they can:

- Draw all of the possible arrays for the number 36;

- List all of the factors of 36.

End-of-Unit Assessment (page 2 of 2)

Problem 2

You have 36 cans of juice.

A. Show all the ways you can arrange these cans into arrays. You may either draw arrays in the space below or use grid paper.

B. List all the factors of 36.

▲ **Resource Masters, M56**

Meeting the Benchmark

These students tend to approach this task in an organized manner that helps them make sure that all of the factors have been listed (e.g., writing the factors in pairs before making the list and then writing the factors in order from either largest to smallest or from smallest to largest).

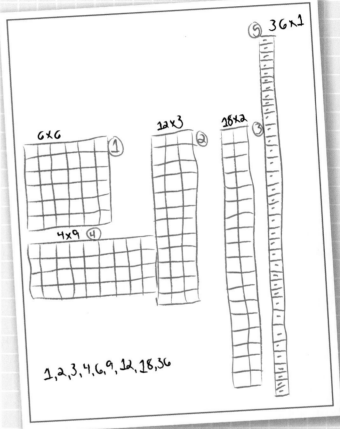

Sample Student Work

Partially Meeting the Benchmark

These students successfully construct most but not all of the arrays for 36 and list most but not all of the factors. They tend to be less organized in their approach to this task, not listing the factors in pairs or in order. For example, they may list 1 as a factor of 36 but fail to include 36 as a factor as well.

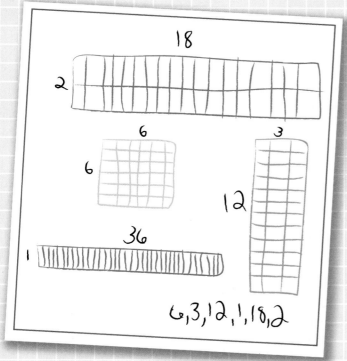

Sample Student Work

Ask these students whether they think they have made all the possible arrays for this number and listed all of the factors. Focus their attention on factor pairs. For example: "You listed 1 as a factor of 36. If 1 is a factor, what other number must be a factor as well? 1 times what equals 36?"

Not Meeting the Benchmark

Students who make no arrays or only a couple of arrays for this number may need more practice in making arrays for numbers smaller than 36. Ask these students to make arrays for the number 12, and help them think about the pairs of factors for this number and how to put these factors in order.

How Many in This Array?

After solving the problem on *Student Activity Book* page 1, *How Many in This Array?*, students are discussing how they determined the number of cans in the open case of juice.

Richard: Sabrina and I solved it by counting by 6, because there are 6 cans going down.

Sabrina: Yeah, it's a 6 by 8 array. There are 8 cans on the top and 6 going down.

Alejandro: I did almost the same thing as Sabrina and Richard. I did 6 × 8 and I skip counted 6, 12, 18, [class joins him] 24, 30, 36, 42, 48.

Marisol: You know how she said that you can count by 6. Well, you can count by 5, too.

Teacher: Marisol has noticed the 6 unobstructed rows of 5 that can be seen on the left side of the array.

Marisol: I counted 5 across and then stopped. I did 5 by 6. 5 × 6 is 30. Then what's left is 3 more in each row and there are 6 rows.

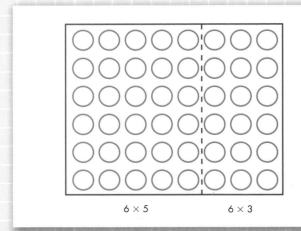

6 × 5   6 × 3

Teacher: So what's 6 × 3?

Marisol struggles a bit, but with some help from her classmates says, "18."

Teacher: So you did 6 × 5 and got 30 and 6 × 3 and got 18. How many cans are in the whole array?

Steve: 30 plus 18 equals 48. There are 48 cans in the array.

Richard: That's the same answer that Sabrina and I got when we counted by 6 eight times.

The teacher records: $(6 \times 5) + (6 \times 3) = 6 \times 8$
$30 + 18 = 48$

Teacher: So there are two different ways that we've solved this problem so far. Sabrina, Alejandro, and Richard saw 6 rows of 8 and thought of the problem as 6 × 8. Marisol saw 6 rows of 5, or 6 × 5, and 6 rows of 3, or 6 × 3, and then put those together. All of them got 48 as their answer.

Breaking apart a more difficult multiplication combination such as 6 × 8 into two simpler combinations such as (6 × 5) + (6 × 3) is an important strategy that students will need as they move into multidigit multiplication problems. Through recording Marisol's strategy for determining the number of cans as an equation equaling 6 × 8, this teacher helped her students see the connection between Marisol's strategy and Richard and Sabrina's strategy.

Another Array Picture

After solving the problem on *Student Activity Book* page 9, *Another Array Picture,* students are discussing how they determined the number of yogurts that would be in the case if it were full.

Amelia: I counted by 12s.

Teacher: Where do you see 12s in this picture?

Amelia points to the full column of three 4-packs on the right side of the picture.

Amelia: There's 12 in each column, because it's 3 times 4. And I can count by twelves: 12, 24, 36, 48, 60, and 72.

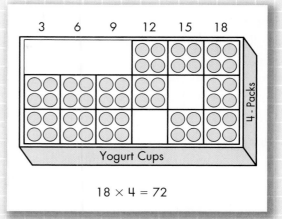

$18 \times 4 = 72$

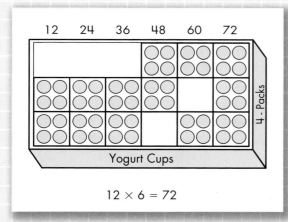

$12 \times 6 = 72$

Bill: I knew that there were 3 there [pointing to the same column of three 4-packs], so I counted by 3 and got 18. [Bill counts the columns in the same way that Amelia did, only by 3s instead of 12s.] Then I multiplied by 4 because there were 4 in each pack. I did 18 times 2 equals 36, and then I doubled it and got 72.

Teacher: Why can Amelia count by 12s and Bill can count by 3s, and they both come up with 72 as the answer?

Yuson: Because Amelia counted the yogurts, and Bill counted the packs.

Luke: It's like they're both counting by 3s, because 12 has 3s in it.

Jill: Yeah, so 3 is a factor of 12, if you can count something by 12s, you can count by 3s.

These students are beginning to make sense of an idea that they will be investigating further in this unit, which is that if one number is a factor of another number, it is also a factor of the multiples of that other number. For now, the teacher acknowledges this and moves on to collect other strategies for solving the problem.

Enrique: I did 12×6, because it's 12 in each column and there are 6 of them. I knew two 12s were 24, then I added 24 plus 24 plus 24.

Cheyenne: I drew 4 in each of the empty places. [She has filled in the missing 4-packs of yogurt so that the array is complete.] I counted them by 5s because that was easier. I got to 90, then I counted all the little packs of 4, and there were 18. So I minused 18 and got 72.

Teacher: Can you explain why you counted by 5s instead of 4s, and why you knew you had to subtract 18 to get your answer?

Cheyenne: I knew there were 4 yogurts in each space, but I don't like counting by 4s. I counted by 5s instead. I knew I added 1 more yogurt each time, so I counted the spaces with yogurt and there were 18. I had to minus 1 yogurt for each space.

Steve: I moved two from the top into the empty spaces, and that made 12 times 4. [Steve has crossed out two of the three 4-packs in the top row and has drawn 4 yogurts in each of the empty spaces in the second and third rows, completing these horizontal rows.] That's 48, then 4 more from the pack left at the top is 52. Then I added 5 empty packs; 5 times 4 is 20, and 52 plus 20 is 72.

In each of these strategies, students are using multiplication combinations that they either already know or can access easily by skip counting. They are considering the array as a whole, despite its missing pieces, and breaking it apart into manageable pieces. All of these are key strategies for solving multiplication problems with larger numbers.

Strategies for Learning Hard Combinations

This class is discussing how to use multiplication combinations they know to find the product of more difficult combinations. The teacher writes 3 × 3 and 3 × 6 on the board.

Teacher: Look at these two problems, 3 × 3 and 3 × 6. You probably know the product of 3 × 3. In fact, you probably know the answer to both of these, but we want to look at the way problems can have connections to each other. We know that 3 × 3 is 9, but how does knowing one math problem help you with solving the other one? If 3 × 3 is 9, how does that help you find the answer to 3 × 6?

Derek: 3 × 3 and 3 × 3 is the same as 3 × 6.

The teacher writes (3 × 3) + (3 × 3) on the board.

Derek: You just combine the two to get 18. 3 × 3 plus 3 × 3 equals 18.

Teacher: So Derek thinks that 3 × 3 plus another 3 × 3 is the same as 3 × 6. Who can suggest a representation of some sort or a story problem that would show that this is true?

Jill: I have a way. You could do an array for 3 × 3 and then just add another 3 × 3 array next to it. Then instead of 3 rows of 3, you have 3 rows of 6. You can count the rows.

The teacher draws two 3 × 3 arrays next to each other on the board as Jill explains. She also places a 3 × 3 Array Card and 3 × 6 Array Card on the overhead to demonstrate the doubling of 3 × 3 to get 3 × 6.

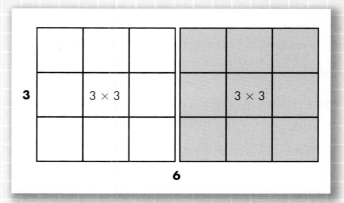

Teacher: Who understands what Jill is saying about the arrays?

Amelia: You can use 3 × 3 and get 9, and all you have to do is add another 9 on it.

Lucy: You're doubling it.

Teacher: What about a story problem? Who could tell a multiplication story that would help us see how 3 × 3 can help with figuring out 3 × 6? . . .

There's quite a long silence, so the teacher then makes a suggestion.

Teacher: Remember when we had the problem about 3-packs of juice? What if we wanted to know how many juice boxes are in six 3-packs of juice? How could knowing 3 × 3 help?

Richard: You know that 3 × 3 is 9, so that's 3 of the packs. But you still have 3 more packs, so, that's 9, and then, um . . . [Richard trails off and seems to have lost track.]

Teacher: How about if I draw this on the board? So here's three 3-packs of juice, and Richard says there are 9 juice boxes in three 3-packs. But we need six 3-packs. So, without drawing the rest, who can continue what Richard started?

Cheyenne: It's just 3 more. It's the same. It's 3 and 3 again. So you have 9, so you'd have the same thing again, another 9, that makes 18.

Students move on to discuss what multiplication combinations they know that can help them solve 8 × 7.

Nadeem: I would do 7 × 7 then plus 7.

Jake: If you knew 10 × 7, which is 70, you could do that and minus 7s or just minus 14.

Teacher: That's an interesting one. Jake says you could start with 10 × 7, which is too big, and then subtract 7s. Who can come up with a story that would help us with this one? You could use the juice cans again or something else.

Alejandro: I know. It's like if you have 8 tables in the cafeteria, and there are 7 kids sitting at each table, and you want to know how many kids. If you had 10 tables, that would be 70 kids, but you have 2 tables less, so you have to take away two of the tables. So 70 minus 7, minus 7.

Anna: You could also do 8 × 5 and then add 8s to it.

Noemi: You could skip count and start at 8 × 2 or start from 0 . . .

Anna: But you could start at 8 × 5 and keep skip counting. That would be quicker.

Teacher: What about doubling? Would that help with this problem? What could you start with?

Nadeem: 4 × 7 is 28.

Jill: It's like what I did before with 3 × 3 and 3 × 6. You could draw a 4 × 7 array and add another 4 × 7 array next to it.

These students are effectively using multiplication combinations they know to solve more difficult problems and are on their way to developing fluency with the basic multiplication combinations. See **Teacher Note:** Learning and Assessing Multiplication Combinations on page 120.

The teacher wants students to get into the habit of using representations and stories to refer to as they reason about multiplication. Even though many of the students in her class can reason about these relatively small numbers without referring to pictures or story problems, she knows that there are some students who need to ground their thinking in such representations.

She also knows that later this year, as students work with breaking apart multiplication problems with larger numbers, many of them will need to have visual images to help them think through which parts of the problem they have solved and which parts they still need to do. By beginning to develop the habit now of creating a picture, diagram, or story, they are learning about important tools to help them reason about multiplication.

Dialogue Box

Identifying Factors and Multiples in *Multiple Turn Over*

Students have just finished playing one game of *Multiple Turn Over*. Before playing a second time, they discuss with the teacher their strategies for determining what factors to choose and which cards to turn over after a factor has been named. They have their recording sheets in front of them.

Ramona: I chose factors that I know would let me turn over a lot of cards. Like 5. I knew I could turn over a lot.

Teacher: So tell me something about 5 that helped you turn over a lot of cards.

Ramona: I had the Multiple Card 65.

Teacher: How did you know that 5 is a factor of 65?

Ramona: I know that 5 is a factor of 60 and if you count by 5 from it, you get 65. I know that if I count by 5, I land on all the multiples of 10 and when I get to 60, I just add 5.

Enrique: For one of my turns, I chose the factor 2, because I had numbers that end in 4, 2, 0, 6, and 8. I knew I would land on those numbers when I count by 2.

Teacher: What do you know about those numbers that you will land on when you count by 2?

Helena: Those are the even numbers.

Derek: I tried not to use 2 as a factor, because then I knew that my partner could turn over a lot of cards, too.

Teacher: So you thought about other factors for the even numbers on your Multiple Cards that you could use instead of 2?

Derek: Yeah. I had 12 and 36 and 60, so I used the factor 6 instead.

Lucy: I had 87 and I thought that 3 might be a factor.

Teacher: How did you decide whether you were right about that?

Lucy: Steve was my partner, and we decided to count by 3 on a number line. We landed on 87, so we knew it was a multiple of 3.

Teacher: Where did you start when you counted on the number line?

Lucy: We started at nine, because we know that 9 is a multiple of 3. We didn't want to start at the very beginning.

Teacher: Could you have started at a higher multiple of 3? How could knowing 10×3 help you?

Steve: Oh! We could have started at 30 because ten 3s would get us to 30.

The teacher writes $10 \times 3 = 30$ and $20 \times 3 = \rule{1cm}{0.4pt}$ on the board.

Teacher: So if you know that ten 3s will get you to 30, how far will twenty 3s get you? How far away from 87 would you be?

Lucy: We would get to 60. That's 27 away—nine more 3s.

The teacher in this classroom helped her students consider how to use known multiplication relationships to identify factors and multiples while playing *Multiple Turn Over*. Although Lucy and Steve's strategy of counting by 3s did result in correctly determining that 3 is a factor of 87, the teacher's questions encouraged them to use known multiplication combinations such as 10×3 and 20×3 to solve the problem more efficiently. Starting with a large "chunk" of the problem is a strategy that will serve students well as they begin multiplying and dividing with larger numbers.

Student Math Handbook

The *Student Math Handbook* pages related to this unit are pictured on the following pages. This book is designed to be used flexibly: as a resource for students doing classwork, as a book students can take home for reference while doing homework and playing math games with their families, and as a reference for families to better understand the work their children are doing in class.

When students take the *Student Math Handbook* home, they and their families can discuss these pages together to reinforce or enhance students' understanding of the mathematical concepts and games in this unit.

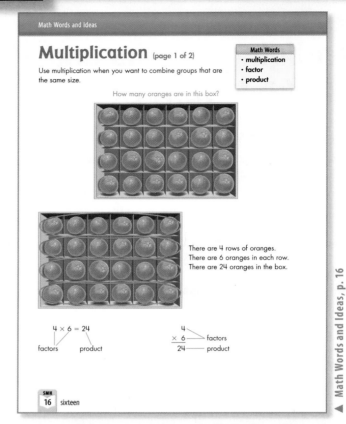

Math Words and Ideas

Multiplication (page 1 of 2)

Math Words
• multiplication
• factor
• product

Use multiplication when you want to combine groups that are the same size.

How many oranges are in this box?

There are 4 rows of oranges.
There are 6 oranges in each row.
There are 24 oranges in the box.

$4 \times 6 = 24$
factors   product

$\times \begin{array}{r} 4 \\ 6 \end{array}$ — factors
24 — product

SMH
16 sixteen

◀ Math Words and Ideas, p. 16

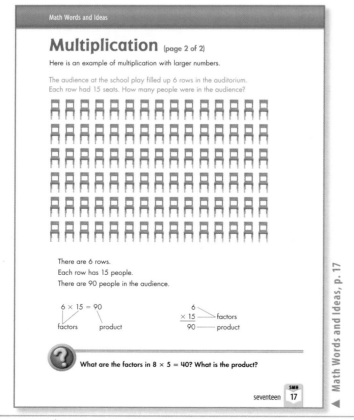

Math Words and Ideas

Multiplication (page 2 of 2)

Here is an example of multiplication with larger numbers.

The audience at the school play filled up 6 rows in the auditorium. Each row had 15 seats. How many people were in the audience?

There are 6 rows.
Each row has 15 people.
There are 90 people in the audience.

$6 \times 15 = 90$
factors   product

$\times \begin{array}{r} 6 \\ 15 \end{array}$ — factors
90 — product

? What are the factors in $8 \times 5 = 40$? What is the product?

seventeen SMH **17**

◀ Math Words and Ideas, p. 17

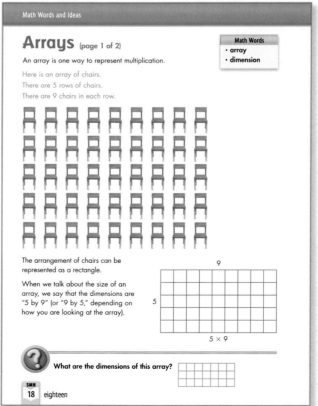

Math Words and Ideas

Arrays (page 1 of 2)

Math Words
• array
• dimension

An array is one way to represent multiplication.

Here is an array of chairs.
There are 5 rows of chairs.
There are 9 chairs in each row.

The arrangement of chairs can be represented as a rectangle.

When we talk about the size of an array, we say that the dimensions are "5 by 9" (or "9 by 5," depending on how you are looking at the array).

9

5

5×9

? What are the dimensions of this array?

SMH **18** eighteen

◀ Math Words and Ideas, p. 18

Math Words and Ideas

Arrays (page 2 of 2)

Here are some examples of rectangular arrays that show how multiplication problems can be broken into smaller parts.

8

7

> This 7 by 8 array can be broken into parts to find the product in many different ways.

8

7 — 7 × 4 — 7 × 4

28 + 28 = 56

8

7 — 7 × 5 — 7 × 3

35 + 21 = 56

8

7 — 5 × 8 — 2 × 8

40 + 16 = 56

8

7 — 4 × 8 — 3 × 8

32 + 24 = 56

All of these arrays show that the product of 7 × 8 is 56.

◀ Math Words and Ideas, p. 19

Math Words and Ideas

Unmarked Arrays (page 1 of 2)

With larger numbers, unmarked arrays can be easier to use than arrays with grid lines. You can imagine the rows of squares without drawing them all.

12
9

12
9

Look at the ways that unmarked arrays are used to show different ways to solve the problem 9 × 12.

12
3 | 3 × 12 = 36 |
9 3 | 3 × 12 = 36 |
3 | 3 × 12 = 36 |

9 × 12 = (3 × 12) + (3 × 12) + (3 × 12)
9 × 12 = 36 + 36 + 36
9 × 12 = **108**

12
6   6
9   9   9
   ×6   ×6
   54   54

9 × 12 = (9 × 6) + (9 × 6)
9 × 12 = 54 + 54
9 × 12 = **108**

12
10   2
9   9   9
   ×10   ×2
   90   18

9 × 12 = (9 × 10) + (9 × 2)
9 × 12 = 90 + 18
9 × 12 = **108**

◀ Math Words and Ideas, p. 20

Math Words and Ideas

Unmarked Arrays (page 2 of 2)

These unmarked arrays show different ways to solve the problem 14 × 20.

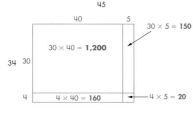
20
10   10
14   14   14
    ×10   ×10
    140   140

140 + 140 = **280**

20
7   7 × 20 = 140
14
7   7 × 20 = 140

140 + 140 = **280**

20
10   10 × 20 = 200
14
4   4 × 20 = 80

200 + 80 = **280**

This unmarked array shows a solution for 34 × 45.

45
40   5
34 30   30 × 40 = **1,200**   30 × 5 = **150**
    4   4 × 40 = 160   4 × 5 = **20**

1,200
160
150
+   20
1,530

34 × 45 = **1,530**

 Use unmarked arrays to show some ways to solve 8 × 14.

◀ Math Words and Ideas, p. 21

Math Words and Ideas

Factors

These three students have different ways to think about factors and different ways to show that 4 is a factor of 32.

Bill: *A factor is a whole number that divides another number evenly, with nothing left over.*

32 ÷ 4 = 8

So I know that 4 is a factor of 32.

Sabrina: *A factor is one of the dimensions of a rectangular array.*

There are 32 tiles here in a 4-by-8 array.

So I know that 4 is a factor of 32.

(And 8 is a factor of 32, too!)

8
4
4 × 8

Derek: *You can skip count by a factor of a number and land exactly on that number.*

I can skip count by 4s to get to 32.
4, 8, 12, 16, 20, 24, 28, 32!

So I know that 4 is a factor of 32.

 What are some other factors of 32?

◀ Math Words and Ideas, p. 22

Factors of 24

These are all the possible rectangular arrays that can be made with 24 square tiles.

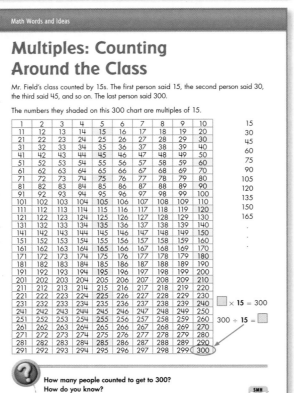

6 × 4 or 4 × 6

2 × 12 or 12 × 2

3 × 8 or 8 × 3

1 × 24 or 24 × 1

Each dimension of these rectangles is a factor of 24.

Listed in order, the factors of 24 are:

1   2   3   4   6   8   12   24

Pairs of factors can be multiplied to get a product of 24.

1 × 24 = 24	2 × 12 = 24	3 × 8 = 24	4 × 6 = 24
24 × 1 = 24	12 × 2 = 24	8 × 3 = 24	6 × 4 = 24

twenty-three **SMH 23**

◀ Math Words and Ideas, p. 23

Multiples

Math Words
· multiples

This 100 chart shows skip counting by 8.

The shaded numbers are multiples of 8.

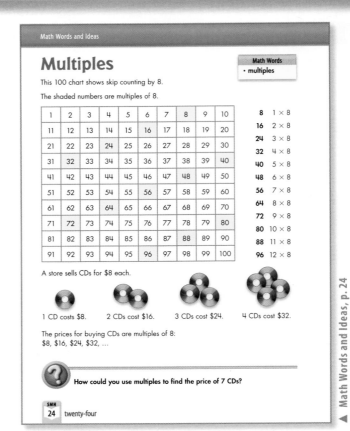

1	2	3	4	5	6	7	8	9	10
11	12	13	14	15	16	17	18	19	20
21	22	23	24	25	26	27	28	29	30
31	32	33	34	35	36	37	38	39	40
41	42	43	44	45	46	47	48	49	50
51	52	53	54	55	56	57	58	59	60
61	62	63	64	65	66	67	68	69	70
71	72	73	74	75	76	77	78	79	80
81	82	83	84	85	86	87	88	89	90
91	92	93	94	95	96	97	98	99	100

8	1 × 8
16	2 × 8
24	3 × 8
32	4 × 8
40	5 × 8
48	6 × 8
56	7 × 8
64	8 × 8
72	9 × 8
80	10 × 8
88	11 × 8
96	12 × 8

A store sells CDs for $8 each.

1 CD costs $8.   2 CDs cost $16.   3 CDs cost $24.   4 CDs cost $32.

The prices for buying CDs are multiples of 8:
$8, $16, $24, $32, …

? How could you use multiples to find the price of 7 CDs?

SMH 24 twenty-four

◀ Math Words and Ideas, p. 24

Multiples: Counting Around the Class

Mr. Field's class counted by 15s. The first person said 15, the second person said 30, the third said 45, and so on. The last person said 300.

The numbers they shaded on this 300 chart are multiples of 15.

1	2	3	4	5	6	7	8	9	10		15
11	12	13	14	15	16	17	18	19	20		30
21	22	23	24	25	26	27	28	29	30		45
31	32	33	34	35	36	37	38	39	40		60
41	42	43	44	45	46	47	48	49	50		75
51	52	53	54	55	56	57	58	59	60		90
61	62	63	64	65	66	67	68	69	70		105
71	72	73	74	75	76	77	78	79	80		120
81	82	83	84	85	86	87	88	89	90		135
91	92	93	94	95	96	97	98	99	100		150
101	102	103	104	105	106	107	108	109	110		165
111	112	113	114	115	116	117	118	119	120		
121	122	123	124	125	126	127	128	129	130		
131	132	133	134	135	136	137	138	139	140		
141	142	143	144	145	146	147	148	149	150		
151	152	153	154	155	156	157	158	159	160		
161	162	163	164	165	166	167	168	169	170		
171	172	173	174	175	176	177	178	179	180		
181	182	183	184	185	186	187	188	189	190		
191	192	193	194	195	196	197	198	199	200		
201	202	203	204	205	206	207	208	209	210		
211	212	213	214	215	216	217	218	219	220		
221	222	223	224	225	226	227	228	229	230		
231	232	233	234	235	236	237	238	239	240		
241	242	243	244	245	246	247	248	249	250		
251	252	253	254	255	256	257	258	259	260		
261	262	263	264	265	266	267	268	269	270		
271	272	273	274	275	276	277	278	279	280		
281	282	283	284	285	286	287	288	289	290		
291	292	293	294	295	296	297	298	299	300		

☐ × 15 = 300

300 ÷ 15 = ☐

? How many people counted to get to 300?
How do you know?

twenty-five **SMH 25**

◀ Math Words and Ideas, p. 25

Factors and Multiples

Consider this list of equations:

4 × 4 = 16	
5 × 4 = 20	
6 × 4 = 24	
7 × 4 = 28	
8 × 4 = 32	
9 × 4 = 36	

4 is a factor of 16, 20, 24, 28, 32, 36, …

4 is a factor of any whole number that it divides evenly.

16, 20, 24, 28, 32, and 36 are some of the multiples of 4.

Multiply 4 by any number to get a multiple of 4.

Arrays can be used to picture factors and multiples.

32 is a multiple of 4, and 4 is a factor of 32. You can use exactly 32 tiles to make a rectangle with one dimension of 4.

30 is *not* a multiple of 4, and 4 is *not* a factor of 30. You cannot use exactly 30 tiles to make a rectangle with one dimension of 4.

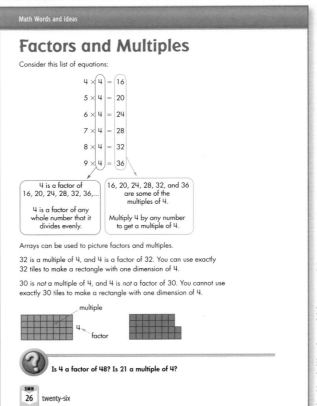

multiple
4
factor

? Is 4 a factor of 48? Is 21 a multiple of 4?

SMH 26 twenty-six

◀ Math Words and Ideas, p. 26

Math Words and Ideas

Prime Numbers

Math Words
- prime number
- composite number

Prime numbers have exactly two factors, 1 and the number itself.

23 is a prime number. The only factors of 23 are 1 and 23. There is only one rectangle that can be made with 23 tiles.

23
1 [_____]
1 × 23 or 23 × 1

Numbers that have more than 2 factors are called composite numbers.

12 is a composite number. There are several pairs of whole numbers that can be multiplied to equal 12.

$$1 \times 12 = 12$$
$$2 \times 6 = 12$$
$$3 \times 4 = 12$$
$$4 \times 3 = 12$$
$$6 \times 2 = 12$$
$$12 \times 1 = 12$$

The number 1 has only one factor. It is neither a prime number nor a composite number.

? Find all the prime numbers up to 50.

twenty-seven **SMH 27**

▲ Math Words and Ideas, p. 27

Math Words and Ideas

Square Numbers

Math Words
- square number

A square number can be represented by a square array.
A square number is made when a number is multiplied by itself.

9 is a square number. 9 tiles can make a square array.

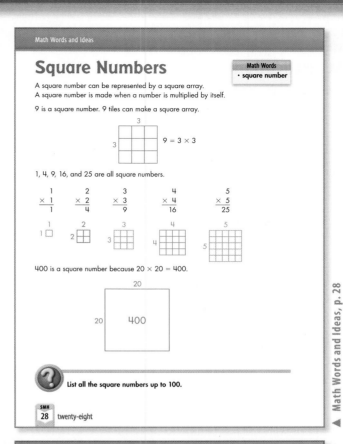

3

3 [grid] 9 = 3 × 3

1, 4, 9, 16, and 25 are all square numbers.

1	2	3	4	5
$\times\ 1$	$\times\ 2$	$\times\ 3$	$\times\ 4$	$\times\ 5$
1	4	9	16	25

400 is a square number because 20 × 20 = 400.

20
20 | 400

? List all the square numbers up to 100.

SMH 28 twenty-eight

▲ Math Words and Ideas, p. 28

Math Words and Ideas

Multiplication Combinations (page 1 of 6)

One of your goals in math class this year is to learn all the multiplication combinations up to 12 × 12.

1 x 1	1 x 2	1 x 3	1 x 4	1 x 5	1 x 6	1 x 7	1 x 8	1 x 9	1 x 10	1 x 11	1 x 12
2 x 1	2 x 2	2 x 3	2 x 4	2 x 5	2 x 6	2 x 7	2 x 8	2 x 9	2 x 10	2 x 11	2 x 12
3 x 1	3 x 2	3 x 3	3 x 4	3 x 5	3 x 6	3 x 7	3 x 8	3 x 9	3 x 10	3 x 11	3 x 12
4 x 1	4 x 2	4 x 3	4 x 4	4 x 5	4 x 6	4 x 7	4 x 8	4 x 9	4 x 10	4 x 11	4 x 12
5 x 1	5 x 2	5 x 3	5 x 4	5 x 5	5 x 6	5 x 7	5 x 8	5 x 9	5 x 10	5 x 11	5 x 12
6 x 1	6 x 2	6 x 3	6 x 4	6 x 5	6 x 6	6 x 7	6 x 8	6 x 9	6 x 10	6 x 11	6 x 12
7 x 1	7 x 2	7 x 3	7 x 4	7 x 5	7 x 6	7 x 7	7 x 8	7 x 9	7 x 10	7 x 11	7 x 12
8 x 1	8 x 2	8 x 3	8 x 4	8 x 5	8 x 6	8 x 7	8 x 8	8 x 9	8 x 10	8 x 11	8 x 12
9 x 1	9 x 2	9 x 3	9 x 4	9 x 5	9 x 6	9 x 7	9 x 8	9 x 9	9 x 10	9 x 11	9 x 12
10 x 1	10 x 2	10 x 3	10 x 4	10 x 5	10 x 6	10 x 7	10 x 8	10 x 9	10 x 10	10 x 11	10 x 12
11 x 1	11 x 2	11 x 3	11 x 4	11 x 5	11 x 6	11 x 7	11 x 8	11 x 9	11 x 10	11 x 11	11 x 12
12 x 1	12 x 2	12 x 3	12 x 4	12 x 5	12 x 6	12 x 7	12 x 8	12 x 9	12 x 10	12 x 11	12 x 12

There are 144 multiplication combinations on this chart. You may think that learning all of them is a challenge. (Remember that last year you learned all of them up to a product of 50.) On the next few pages you will find some suggestions to help you learn the multiplication combinations.

As you practice these multiplication combinations, make two lists like those shown.

Combinations I Know	Combinations I'm Working On

twenty-nine **SMH 29**

▲ Math Words and Ideas, p. 29

Math Words and Ideas

Multiplication Combinations (page 2 of 6)

Learning two combinations at a time

To help you learn multiplication combinations, think about two combinations at a time, such as 8 × 3 and 3 × 8.

These two problems look different, but have the same answer.

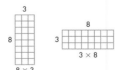

3
8 [grid]
8 × 3

8
3 [grid]
3 × 8

When you know that 8 × 3 = 24, you also know that 3 × 8 = 24.

You have learned two multiplication combinations!

By "turning around" combinations and learning them two at a time, the chart of multiplication combinations is reduced from 144 to 78 combinations to learn!

1 x 1	1 x 2	1 x 3	1 x 4	1 x 5	1 x 6	1 x 7	1 x 8	1 x 9	1 x 10	1 x 11	1 x 12
2 x 1 2 x 2	2 x 2	2 x 3	2 x 4	2 x 5	2 x 6	2 x 7	2 x 8	2 x 9	2 x 10	2 x 11	2 x 12
3 x 1 3 x 2	3 x 2 3 x 3	3 x 3	3 x 4	3 x 5	3 x 6	3 x 7	3 x 8	3 x 9	3 x 10	3 x 11	3 x 12
4 x 1 4 x 3	4 x 2 4 x 3	4 x 3 4 x 4	4 x 4	4 x 5	4 x 6	4 x 7	4 x 8	4 x 9	4 x 10	4 x 11	4 x 12
5 x 1 5 x 5	5 x 2 5 x 4	5 x 3 5 x 4	5 x 4 5 x 5	5 x 5	5 x 6	5 x 7	5 x 8	5 x 9	5 x 10	5 x 11	5 x 12
6 x 1 6 x 6	6 x 2 6 x 4	6 x 3 6 x 5	6 x 4 6 x 6	6 x 5 6 x 6	6 x 6	6 x 7	6 x 8	6 x 9	6 x 10	6 x 11	6 x 12
7 x 1 7 x 7	7 x 2 7 x 4	7 x 3 7 x 5	7 x 4 7 x 7	7 x 5 7 x 7	7 x 6 7 x 7	7 x 7	7 x 8	7 x 9	7 x 10	7 x 11	7 x 12
8 x 1 8 x 8	8 x 2 8 x 3	8 x 3 8 x 4	8 x 4 8 x 8	8 x 5 8 x 8	8 x 6 8 x 8	8 x 7 8 x 8	8 x 8	8 x 9	8 x 10	8 x 11	8 x 12
9 x 1 9 x 9	9 x 2 9 x 3	9 x 3 9 x 4	9 x 4 9 x 9	9 x 5 9 x 9	9 x 6 9 x 9	9 x 7 9 x 9	9 x 8 9 x 9	9 x 9	9 x 10	9 x 11	9 x 12
10 x 1 10 x 10	10 x 2 10 x 10	10 x 3 10 x 10	10 x 4 10 x 10	10 x 5 10 x 10	10 x 6 10 x 10	10 x 7 10 x 10	10 x 8 10 x 10	10 x 9 10 x 10	10 x 10	10 x 11	10 x 12
11 x 1 11 x 11	11 x 2 11 x 11	11 x 3 11 x 11	11 x 4 11 x 11	11 x 5 11 x 11	11 x 6 11 x 11	11 x 7 11 x 11	11 x 8 11 x 11	11 x 9 11 x 11	11 x 10 11 x 11	11 x 11	11 x 12
12 x 1 12 x 12	12 x 2 12 x 12	12 x 3 12 x 12	12 x 4 12 x 12	12 x 5 12 x 12	12 x 6 12 x 12	12 x 7 12 x 12	12 x 8 12 x 12	12 x 9 12 x 12	12 x 10 12 x 12	12 x 11 12 x 12	12 x 12

SMH 30 thirty

▲ Math Words and Ideas, p. 30

Math Words and Ideas

Multiplication Combinations (page 3 of 6)

A helpful way to learn multiplication combinations is to think about one category at a time. Here are some categories you may have seen before. You probably already know many of these combinations.

Learning the ×1 combinations

You may be thinking about only one group.

1 group of 9 equals 9

$\rightarrow$ 1 × 9 = 9

You may also be thinking about many groups of 1.

6 groups of 1 equal 6

$\rightarrow$ 6 × 1 = 6

Learning the ×2 combinations

Multiplying by 2 is the same as doubling a number.

$\rightarrow$ 8 + 8 = 16

$\rightarrow$ 2 × 8 = 16

Learning the ×10 and ×5 combinations

You can learn these combinations by skip counting by 10s and 5s.

10, 20, 30, 40, 50, 60 $\rightarrow$ 6 × 10 = 60

5, 10, 15, 20, 25, 30 $\rightarrow$ 6 × 5 = 30

Another way to find a ×5 combination is to remember that it is half of a ×10 combination.

6 × 10 = 60   6 × 5 = 30

6 × 5 (or 30) is half of 6 × 10 (or 60).

thirty-one **31**

◀ Math Words and Ideas, p. 31

Math Words and Ideas

Multiplication Combinations (page 4 of 6)

Here are some more categories to help you learn the multiplication combinations.

Learning the ×11 Combinations

Many students learn these combinations by noticing the double-digit pattern they create.

11	11	11	11	11
×3	×4	×5	×6	×7
33	44	55	66	77

Learning the ×12 Combinations

Many students multiply by 12 by breaking the 12 into 10 and 2.

6 × 12 = (6 × 10) + (6 × 2)
6 × 12 = 60 + 12
6 × 12 = 72

6 × 10 = 60   6 × 2 = 12

Learning the Square Numbers

Many students remember the square number combinations from experiences building the squares with tiles or drawing them on grid paper.

3	4	5	6
×3	×4	×5	×6
9	16	25	36

7	8	9
×7	×8	×9
49	64	81

32 thirty-two

◀ Math Words and Ideas, p. 32

Math Words and Ideas

Multiplication Combinations (page 5 of 6)

After you have used all these categories to practice the multiplication combinations, you have only a few more to learn.

1×1	1×2	1×3	1×4	1×5	1×6	1×7	1×8	1×9	1×10	1×11	1×12
2×1	2×2	2×3	2×4	2×5	2×6	2×7	2×8	2×9	2×10	2×11	2×12
3×1	3×2	3×3	3×4	3×5	3×6	3×7	3×8	3×9	3×10	3×11	3×12
4×1	4×2	4×3	4×4	4×5	4×6	4×7	4×8	4×9	4×10	4×11	4×12
5×1	5×2	5×3	5×4	5×5	5×6	5×7	5×8	5×9	5×10	5×11	5×12
6×1	6×2	6×3	6×4	6×5	6×6	6×7	6×8	6×9	6×10	6×11	6×12
7×1	7×2	7×3	7×4	7×5	7×6	7×7	7×8	7×9	7×10	7×11	7×12
8×1	8×2	8×3	8×4	8×5	8×6	8×7	8×8	8×9	8×10	8×11	8×12
9×1	9×2	9×3	9×4	9×5	9×6	9×7	9×8	9×9	9×10	9×11	9×12
10×1	10×2	10×3	10×4	10×5	10×6	10×7	10×8	10×9	10×10	10×11	10×12
11×1	11×2	11×3	11×4	11×5	11×6	11×7	11×8	11×9	11×10	11×11	11×12
12×1	12×2	12×3	12×4	12×5	12×6	12×7	12×8	12×9	12×10	12×11	12×12

As you practice all of the multiplication combinations, there will be some that you "just know" and others that you are "working on" learning.

One way to practice a combination that is hard for you is to make a Multiplication Clue Card. Think of a combination you already know that you can start with to help you learn the harder one.

You will make your own Multiplication Cards for combinations that are hard for you.

On the next page are examples of Multiplication Cards made by students to help them learn 7 × 8 and 8 × 7.

```
7 × 8
8 × 7

Start with _____
```

thirty-three **33**

◀ Math Words and Ideas, p. 33

Math Words and Ideas

Multiplication Combinations (page 6 of 6)

Like many fourth graders, these students think that 7 × 8 is a hard multiplication combination to learn. Each of these students has a different strategy to solve 7 × 8. They use a multiplication combination that they know to help them solve 7 × 8.

Neomi: *I would do 7 × 7 and then add 7.*

7 × 7

$$\begin{array}{r} 49 \\ + 7 \\ \hline 56 \end{array}$$

```
7 × 8
8 × 7

Start With    7 × 7
              Neomi
```

Alejandro: *I would double a 7 by 4 array to make 7 × 8.*

7 × 4   7 × 4

$$\begin{array}{r} 7 \\ × 4 \\ \hline 28 \end{array}$$

20 + 20 + 8 + 8 = 56
40   +   16 = 56

```
7 × 8
8 × 7

Start With    7 × 4
              Alejandro
```

Ramona: *I think of it as seven 8s. I would start at 5 × 8 and keep skip counting by 8s.*

5 × 8

5 × 8 = 40

40 + 8 = 48
48 + 8 = 56

```
7 × 8
8 × 7

Start With    5 × 8
              Ramona
```

34 thirty-four

◀ Math Words and Ideas, p. 34

Top-left panel

Multiplying Groups of 10

(page 1 of 2)

Each of these models helps show the relationship between these two multiplication equations.

$$3 \times 4 = 12$$
$$3 \times 40 = 120$$

Cubes

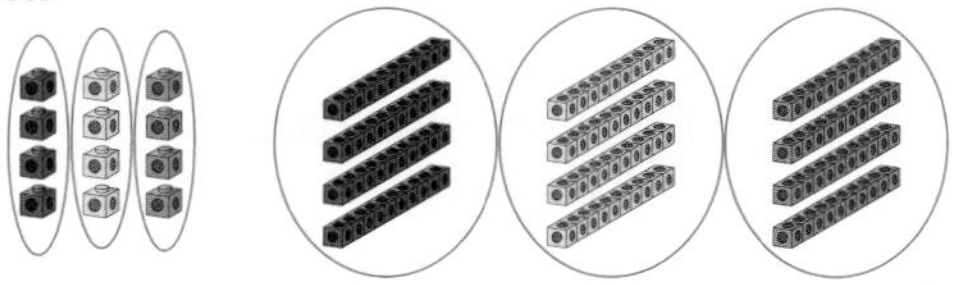

3 groups of 4 cubes   3 groups of 40 cubes

Arrays

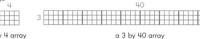

a 3 by 4 array   a 3 by 40 array

Skip Counting Patterns

This pattern of multiples increases by 4.

Multiples of 4:   4   8   (12)   16   20   24   28   32   36   40 . . .

This pattern of multiples increases by 4 tens.

Multiples of 40:   40   80   (120)   160   200   240   280   320   360   400 . . .

thirty-seven **37**

▲ Math Words and Ideas, p. 37

Top-right panel

Multiplying Groups of 10

(page 2 of 2)

Consider the relationship among these three equations.

$$3 \times 4 = \quad 12$$
$$3 \times 40 = \quad 120$$
$$30 \times 40 = 1,200$$

$3 \times 4 = 12$	$3 \times 4 = 12$
$3 \times 40 = 120$	 $(3 \times 4) \times 10 = 12 \times 10$
$30 \times 40 = 1,200$	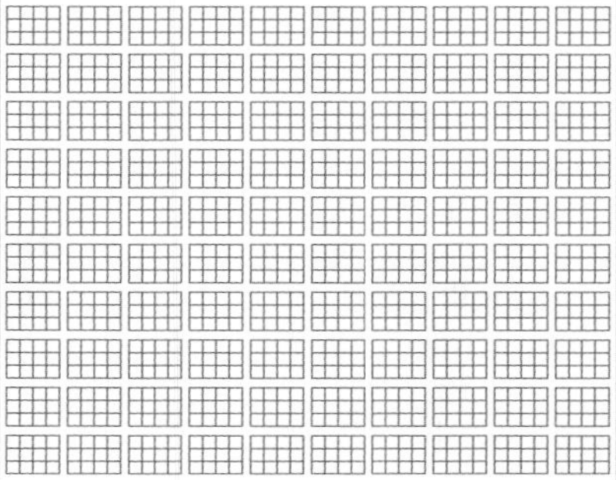 $(3 \times 4) \times (10 \times 10) = 12 \times 100$

Solve these related problems.
$5 \times 7 =$ _____ 5×70 _____ $50 \times 70 =$ _____

38 thirty-eight

▲ Math Words and Ideas, p. 38

Bottom-left panel

Factor Pairs

You need

- set of Array Cards

Play alone or with a partner.

1. Spread out all of the Array Cards in front of you. All cards should have the dimensions side faceup.

2. Choose an Array Card and put your finger on it. Say the number of squares in the array if you know it. (Don't pick up the card until you say the answer.) If you don't know the number of squares, use a strategy to figure it out. Find a way to figure out how many squares there are without counting every one.

3. Turn the card over to check your answer. If your answer is correct, then you get to keep the card.

4. If you are playing with a partner, take turns choosing cards and finding the number of squares in each array.

5. The game is over when you have picked up all the cards.

6. While you are playing, make lists for yourself of "Combinations I Know" and "Combinations I'm Working On." You'll be using these lists to help you learn your multiplication combinations.

G6

▲ Games, G6

Bottom-right panel

Multiple Turn Over

You need

- deck of Multiple Cards
- calculators (optional)
- *Multiple Turn Over* Recording Sheet

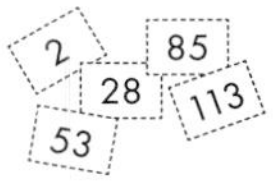

Basic Game: Numbers 2–50
Intermediate Game: Numbers 2–80
Advanced Game: Numbers 2–113

Play with a partner or in a small group.

1. Deal out ten Multiple Cards to each player.

2. Players arrange their Multiple Cards faceup in front of them. Each player should be able to see everyone's Multiple Cards.

3. The player with the smallest multiple begins. This player calls out any whole number (except 1). Each player records that factor on his or her *Multiple Turn Over* Recording Sheet.

4. All the players (including the player who called out the number) search for cards in their set that are multiples of that number. They write those multiples on their recording sheet and turn those cards facedown. If a player has no multiples of a number called, that player writes "none" under "Multiple Cards I Turned Over."

5. Players take turns calling out numbers. The game is over when one player turns over all ten Multiple Cards.

G9

▲ Games, G9

Index